Madonna and Other Spectacles

BOOKS BY HAROLD JAFFE

MADONNA

AND

OTHER SPECTACLES

FICTIONS BY

HAROLD JAFFE

PAJ PUBLICATIONS
NEW YORK

Library of Congress Cataloging in Publication Data
Madonna and Other Spectacles
Library of Congress Catalog Card No.: 87-73277
ISBN: 1-55554-025-2

Printed in the United States of America

Publication of this book has been made possible in part by grants received from the National Endowment for the Arts, Washington, D.C., a federal agency, and the New York State Council on the Arts.

ACKNOWLEDGEMENTS: Several of these fictions were published in *Performing Arts Journal, Mississippi Review, Chelsea, New Virginia Review, Exquisite Corpse, Central Park, Boundary 2, Fiction International,* and *Border Literature: A Bi-National Anthology.*

The epigraph in ''Tonto'' is from Brecht's ''The Measures Taken,'' in *The Jewish Wife and Other Plays,* Ed. and trans. by Eric Bentley (Grove Press, 1965).

for
M. J.

CONTENTS

MADONNA AND OTHER SPECTACLES

<u>ONE</u>

MADONNA

wanted to live in the San Remo, a hincty high-rise in New York City, but her application was turned down by the tenant-owners, including other celebs, though Madonna appeared at the crucial interview with three crucifixes around her neck, or maybe it was four, she had (she is firm on this point) a "very" Catholic childhood, so that her *nom de video,* Madonna, serves the practical dual purpose of alloy and allegory, each encouraged and denied, likewise in her smash-hit single "Material Girl," material is of course lucre while being a timely reminder of our composition as vile matter, ditto Madonna's participation in a '79 soft-core flick in the Big Apple for which she was paid the princely sum of $100, and what was billed as the real scuz was not-so-deftly simulated, ditto her nudie photos disinterred, but my dialectical (so to speak) gloss on U.S. iconizing-commodifying was evidently lost on Paul Simon, Dustin Hoffman and the others on the application committee of the San Remo, the higher you climb the ladder of success the more your (pardon my Greek) arse is exposed applies in spades to Madonna, though she'd rather expose her navel, I've seen more female navels in rainy London this summer, Madonna-invoked, than you would imagine: Earl's Court, Shoreditch, Chelsea, King's Cross, saw a brace on Princess Street, Edinburgh, in the pouring rain, why *shouldn't* she issue a "restraining order" on the redistribution of her porn flick, on the publication of her nudies in both *Penthouse* and *Playboy,* the year was '79 (Before AIDS), Hamilton Jordan was deftly counseling Jimmy Carter on "Human Rights," Madonna was an eighteen-year-old tyro called Louise Ciccone, slim but breasty, brown hair and lush bush and sexy hair on her belly and lots under her arms, her "look" Lower-East-Side-sulky, even then she was religious as heck, in her way, only Diane Keaton among the bigs voted Yea on Madonna's application to live in the San Remo, perhaps on the grounds of sisterhood, I can only speculate, perhaps on the grounds of charity, we are in the grip of BAND AID, aid to the strife-torn in Africa, if only those Marxists would let our dollars get through to the folks that need them: the good poor (in Matthew Arnold's father's phrase), Poverty Sucks, like the bumper-sticker says, but isn't it just the incentive you need to get rich, a buffer (I mean poverty) against getting poor, as AIDS discourages congress with Haitians, homos, hemos, so wear your necktie munch on irradiated bean sprouts phone your broker *don't* bend over, "Like a Virgin," Madonna's first mega-smash, has got it all if you alter the words, while inserting Mother Teresa in her habit for Madonna in her confection of silks, no big deal, not with our technology, I think of the poor when I eat Tandoori, you wouldn't believe how many Indian/Pakistani restaurants there are throughout the U.K., Sikhs though scarce, evidently because of their continuing dispute with India, because of their stubborn insistence on possessing their skins, tough for a male Sikh to hide when you think of it, appearance isn't everything, well, it's darn close, take Madonna's navel, truthfully I prefer reading about her navel from a distance, the U.K. isn't distant enough, and I'd prefer reading about her navel in another language, Basque, say, or Punjabi (as spoken by the Sikhs in northwest India), Gosh, she's the very reincarnation of Marilyn Monroe, a tramp with style, a composite of styles, a xeroxed composite of apparent styles accessed, video'd, transmitted via satellite, take the incessant rain in London, filthy weather and the thing is we have the technology to do something about it, the Brits though would like it both ways: the Queen Mother at Ascot and creeping Americanization on the telly, "Dallas" reruns are all the rage, "MERRY MPs DANGLED A TOPLESS GIRL OVER THE RIVER THAMES IN A STAGGERING EARLY-HOURS RAVE-UP" [this wasn't

Madonna though it might have been], "ONE LABOUR
MEMBER SWUNG THE GIGGLING GIRL OVER THE
EDGE OF THE COMMONS TERRACE WITH HIS ARMS
ROUND HER LEGS—AND SUDDENLY HER CHARMS
POPPED OUT," according to *The Sun,* but why Madonna
rather than video'd chanteuses like Blondie or Sade (pronounced "Sharday"), well, consider her hair, I think of Ber-
nini's St. Theresa in her passion, or Barbara Stanwyck in a 40s
betrayed-husband flick with moody camera angles, polymorphous perversity, A.C.-D.C. and whatever other C's you
come up with (these *are* the pluralistic, pentecostal 80s),
Madonna's hair—I want to put this plainly—is, like Ahab's
doubloon, everything to everybody and nothing, like the
foamy head of my draft Guinness, without the draft, now if we
can only convince our Secretary of Defense, who, like
Madonna, as of this writing, is on a bad roll, he's an honorable
man, a proud man, and when he closes his eyes to respond to a
question we know that the teleprompter on the inside of his
eyelids will be American-made, without Japanese anything, I
imagine the unwinding of a bloody bandage and underneath,
red and never not festering: *Communism* (reads the teleprompter) in *Our* hemisphere, when the talk turns to politics
Madonna and her entourage commence to yawn, and who can
blame them?, like that enduring silliness about what does the
Scottie wear under his kilt, here in Inverness where I'm nurs-
ing my pint (it's late morning but raining bullets), I scan the
OxBridge weeklies wherein the splenetic-exotic Scot is as ever
good sport, as the Hindus under the Raj, as the "kaffirs" to the
Afrikaners, but note: there is, as the intelligent writer demon-
strated conclusively in a *New Yorker* article a while back, a
distinct though subtle difference between fashion and style,
the latter as you might expect being the more refined species,
where then would you situate Madonna?, don't answer too
quickly, don't answer surely on the basis of Madonna repre-
senting "low" as against "high" culture, I'm tempted to quote
the playwright Tom Stoppard but compositionally I can't fit
him in, here he is: "There's an essential distinction between
countries where the abuse of human rights represents the

system in triumph, and the countries in which it represents the failure of the system," Stoppard of course is clever and wealthy, and clever about being wealthy, beneath his neat formulation resides the oak-panelled soul of OxBridge, Sandhurst too, I remind you that it was not in benighted Moscow nor in Pretoria's whited sepulchre nor in Managua Nicaragua, but in the demotic Big Apple where they denied Madonna, oh well, it's Thursday and I'm off to the National Film Institute to see Joseph Losey's remake of Fritz Lang's *M,* and what can one say that hasn't been said about the ringworm of child molestation, is it really happening?, is it lurid imagining erected on lurid imagining in the service of classic-formula COKE and the New Old Vigilance?, Losey did his *M,* in '51, twenty years after Lang, with (improbably) David Wayne in the Peter Lorre role, Losey, you recall, an American who did most of his strong work in England, best known for his collusion with Pinter in *The Servant,* Pinter incidentally just back from Turkey where he and Monroe's ex, Arthur Miller, were sent by PEN to pose certain queries about the systematic violation of certain Turkish artists' human rights, Pinter didn't hit it off with the American ambassador, in fact exchanged vivid Pinteresque insults, slinging at each other from a stagey distance, the ambassador with the provisional last word: Pinter was incapable, he put it, of seeing Turkey's policy "in the round," which evidently is our Secretary of Defense's position, judging from his recent teleprompted remarks re Turkey's "alleged" genocide of Armenians, the Secretary's guiding principle/missile here being Turkey's good will re U.S. bases in Turkey to bolster defense against Communism world-wide and intergalactically as well since the Soviets are, please remember, Asiatics, possessing that Asian mentality derived from Attila, limitless aggression, absolutely, Madonna about the eyes is Asian, dancing in circles like a benign ringworm, like a houri or odalisque, she doesn't touch us like Mary Pickford, touch is scarcely the point, nor is her coolness Garbo's with its insinuation of depths, Madonna glitters like neon viewed from the wrong side of the scope, she's there and not there, making contact with our nervous system like an electrified dentist's

implement tap-tapping our tooth, no longer "the victim's information, but the *victim,* that torture needs to win—or reduce to
powerlessness. By expanding the types and frequency of torture, by acquiring and exploiting a more exact knowledge of
psychology and neurology, torture in the late 20th century has
become able to inflict an immense variety of relatively graded
degrees of pain upon anyone" (Edward Peters, *Torture,* Black-
well, '85), here in the U.K. there are only four television
channels (though satellite dish antennas are making their bid)
but any number of labels of beer, what happened to that
honest mug of English bitter that is not ice-cold after the
American fashion?, let's face it, short of cauterization (large-
scale), homogenization American-style (Japanese-accented) is
irresistible, and, yes, it is up to the artist (the who?) to extract,
extrapolate, extort the esthetic principle no longer orbiting
neck-deep in contaminant, such an immense variety of flavors,
besides you can blend them yourselves, Madonna is (grant me
this trope) a dervish, her mobile navel, slender, spike-heeled
feet administering delicately graded degrees of pain, her Asian
eyes, polymorphous hair (since shorn), her broader and
broader wake of agents and investment advisers, which is
probably the toughest job of the lot given the wild fluctuation
of the dollar, mind you, I'm not implying that there aren't
good, sound, economic heads in control: rock-solid Volcker at
the Fed, the incorruptible Stockman, who was a peace activist
in the Sixties and recently left the administration for Wall
Street and a real salary (seven figures allegedly), Reagan's
Doppel Regan (exorcized in the wake of "Irangate"), the estimable Meese (he's at Justice but ranges widely), who then
are our torturers? Well, I'd like to cite Arendt's banality of evil
(you thought I'd have something off-the-wall up my sleeve), in
fact it's more appropriate than ever, dissociate while administering pain hi-ho, in front of the console, phoning your broker, stroking your hairless leg, "evil" itself can stand redefin-
ing, which perhaps I'll get to, though in a roundabout way,
since it is harder than ever to be plain, that is, *you* are plain but
is it plain that's received?, heck no, the language all unstuck,
thus Madonna and her whirling navel will describe a broad

sphere of effluence, so to speak, inflicting all species of pleasure, so to speak, and if this seems elusive, take heart, there
are these constants: dollars and power, though their acquisi-
tion and implementation signify a more various collusion,
collusion in what?, in keeping the good poor good and poor, in
keeping the electrified wire (now wireless) hooked to your
genitals, yes yours.

U.K., 6.85
U.S., 9.86, 8.87

THE THREE STOOGES

"All the decisive blows are struck left-handed"
Walter Benjamin

You're intelligent.
I was smarter nine years ago.
You're mercurial.
You should have seen me in '68.

Shemp came first, dropped out in favor of Curly, then took Curly's place after Curly's stroke in '46: Moe Howard, Shemp Howard, Curly Howard, Larry Fine, especially Moe/Curly/ Larry, Jews (in high relief), brothers from Brooklyn, except Larry from Philly, THEY'RE IN THE GIRL'S BATHROOM, Curly in outsize frock and dummy boobs goes in first, Moe slaps Larry to ask where Curly went, Larry's about to protest when he's slapped again—fronthand, backhand—nose tweaked, shin kicked, meanwhile from the little girl's room, squeals of chagrin and delight, simultaneous double-take by Moe and Larry, they're on their way

You're soulful.
What's that?
You don't know what soulful is?
Sonny Boy Williamson?
That's right.
Bessie Smith?
Right.
They're dead.
Sonny Boy Williamson is dead?
I'm pretty sure he is.

(Pause)
What's that albino reggae star's name? Yellowman?
Yellow Mama.
What's that?
It's what black death-row inmates call the electric chair in Alabama.

all three now in the girl's bathroom, Moe mistaking Curly for the real article, commences to flirt, Larry bumblingly follows suit, and now Moe and Larry are competing for Ms. Curly's affections in the little girl's room of the junior high school, lush May, heartland America, scrubbed white young sperm, Hollywood time warp, cutesy freckles, Moe chucks Larry three quick chucks under the chin (in "real life" Moe Howard bullied Larry Fine), gouges his eyes, bops him on the bean, Curly meanwhile coyly posing, we're still in the little girl's room, but when Moe the victor attempts to embrace "her"

You're an avid sports fan.
I'm American. Americans love sports. In a poll conducted by *Sports Illustrated* seventy-three percent of all Americans characterized themselves as sports fans.
(Pause)
What's your favorite sport?
Billiards. Three balls on a green smooth ground. No pockets.
No pockets?
None.

he comes in contact with a bristly cheek, uh-oh, something ain't right here, then Moe notices a striped trouser leg beneath the frock, what's this, at which juncture Curly, panicked, emits his celebrated castrato woo-woo-woo-woo, even as he is violently unfrocked by Moe and Larry, spun about, bopped-tweaked-chucked-gouged-thumped, SLOW DISSOLVE, in this frame they're in church in short pants, Curly's dimply, Larry's hairy, Moe's knobby knees, back pew, mouths agape, devouring with their eyes

You're funny. Mordantly funny. I like that about you.

I was funnier in '68. Less mordant.

Do you have hope?

I have a vestigial Buddhism which counsels against hope which it equates with desire.

Is that bad, desire?

The Buddhist sense is of striving, coveting. Natural, so to speak, desire is fine presumably.

(Pause)

The very word, Buddhism, has an odd ring about it these days.

It's lost, in the west, its populist base.

Name me a populist.

Pete Rose.

He caught Cobb, didn't he?

He's a white ballplayer who knows a bit of what it feels like to be a non-white ballplayer. Of course he's management now.

Name me another populist.

Lester Maddox, but he's got AIDS. George Wallace, but he's kaput below the waist. Muhammad Ali, but he's brain-damaged.

Hang on. Lester Maddox *doesn't* have AIDS. He called a news conference to say so. He thought he had contracted the scourge from a black blood donor, in the Bahamas, where he had gone for a controversial cancer treatment. It was a false alarm.

a pinup mag beneath their shared missal, Curly in particular making lip-smacking sounds of approval, loud enough to disturb the other parishioners, loud enough eventually to alert the Pastor, who casts a pointed look, then another, stumbling at his sermon, THEY HAVE SOWN THE WIND / THEY SHALL REAP THE WHIRLWIND, *Hosea* 8:7, the boys, hornily into porn, won't be denied, the pastor ceases sermonizing, parishioners peevishly turned to the Stooges, whose ejaculations of approval are now uncontrolled, competing for the closest look at the pinup mag, and now they're fighting for it, Curly has it, has climbed into the pew in front, blundered his way into the aisle, Moe and Larry in hot pursuit, the parishioners still immobile, except for a brawny, hyper-respectable, middle-aged male, who resembles Patrick Buchanan, Agnew's now Reagan's kapo speechifier, loves a good fight, for a good cause, packs his ideology in a thigh holster, dum-dum bullets, white American nuclear family, dog-flag-money-Disney, not just any dog, he sounds the alarm, and now the parishioners, man, woman, child and dog, are in pursuit of the Stooges, in the ripening meadow, goldenrod, late summer, Sunday a.m.

Who is that gaunt man with the mohawk haircut and live chicken on his tattooed shoulder? He's squatting on that roof smoking cigarettes and spitting into a coffee tin.

He resembles DeNiro in *Taxi Driver,* right?

I guess so.

The tattoo is a product endorsement. So is the coffee tin. He's got an MBA from Oral Roberts. He bashes AIDS victims.

(Pause)

He's gotten up. What's he doing?

He's shuffling on archless feet across the deserted artery kicking a chunk of bone and whistling a patriotic air on pitch. Absolutely on pitch.

pursuing the misfits, as if riding to hounds, as in Fritz Lang's *M,* Keystone Kapos, except after a particular sharp turn the Stooges, swarthy, naked, wearing greasy headcloths, squatting on their heels on a low broad rock, are waiting for them with Uzis, AK 47s, and now the Stooges, yipping, shrieking, are spraying the parishioners with bullets, shouting slogans, squatting, spraying

You're a dreamer.

Yes.

Even now.

Yes.

Do you sleep in the nude?

I dream in the nude.

You'll never get a product endorsement.

You're wrong.

How so?

New formula Coke has a contingency plan. So does EX-XON and Ma Bell and Xerox and Manville (they're the asbestos folks). It has to do with AIDS sufferers and Gypsies and Shamans and housewives, in the event they, or any of them, become marketable.

bodies toppling, no blood, this is a cartoon, this is Disney, American-made, Economy-sized blah-blah, TRACK OUT / SLOW DISSOLVE, the boys are house-painters, carrying ladders, paints, rollers, maneuvering through Wall Street, hired to whitewash a facade of the Stock Exchange, lunch-time, they decide to pause, have a bite, which they do on the milling sidewalk, within view of the Stock Exchange, opening their metal lunch pails, squabbling over which one gets the salami sandwich, Moe wins that squabble, sipping coffee from a thermos, wolfing the chow, then unveiling the devil's-food cake, workaholic money-mavens compelled to swerve, bristle at the Stooges' invasion of their sidewalk, it is after all Wall Street, home of the brave / investor, peevish words exchanged, Stooges give as good as they get, but now the scene has changed, they're painting the eastern facade, above a broad window that looks into the world-famous, frantic-manic-orgasmic Exchange floor, today's a biggie, in keen anticipation of America's entering the War

I'll risk a platitude. I see it—I mean the peopled world—as the glass half-full or half-empty thing. There's enormous shittiness all right, but perception contributes to the shittiness.

You mean we could, one, employ the genocidal dead as fertilizer and grow more tobacco, or, two, stack them, mourn them, let them decompose?

(Pause)

All right, I put it banally. But isn't the notion of perception Buddhist?

Is genocide perception?

No, of course not. But is genocide chronic?
You tell me.

now the Stooges are as patriotic as the next fellow, hot dog /
you bet, still the shirtsleeved traders on the Exchange floor
brandishing chits, shouting, milling about or scurrying, look
ridiculous, and the boys begin to pay more attention to them
than to the whitewashing, unaware that one of the large cans
has overturned, that the white paint is seeping through the
partially opened window, down one of the broad walls of the
Stock Exchange, which is bad enough but becomes a real pain
when inadvertently Curly kicks over a second can, which is
suspended in such a way that it is dripping onto the heads and
noses and neckties of the traders who are so caught up in their
trading that it takes some time for them to notice, but eventually they notice, looking up, thinking big-bird, thinking Russia, though the ostensible enemy is Nazi Germany, finally
spotting the culprits, bemused amused loonies, in point of fact
they're hysterical, Moe on one ladder, Curly and Larry on
another, poking each other in the sides, Curly *nyuck, nyuck,
nyucking,* loving the chagrin of the whitewashed traders, red in
the face, brandishing

You're better than you take yourself to be.
Ah.
Your flashy, mordant cynicism is just a stalking horse. It's
you who's behind it, with a bomb and a principle.
I see.
Except, like a Shiite, the bomb is strapped to your waist.
Like Conrad's ascetic revolutionary in *The Secret Agent*.
It needs only to be unstrapped without being detonated.
What is the principle?
Collective action. What else can it be?
Violent collective action?
If need be.
Who determines the "need"?

chits, and now the inevitable happens: the Stooges topple

headlong from their ladders onto the Stock Exchange floor trailing white paint and turpentine, apoplectic traders in pursuit, on top of and under the long tables, where much of the great business of this great nation is transacted, meanwhile a big-league trader, having just completed a profitable transaction in "futures," lights a cheroot, tosses the match onto the Floor, it ignites some turpentine-soaked chits, the flames spread very rapidly, it's a holocaust, with a lower or upper case "h," depending on the length and breadth of your nose, and melanin, amber waves of / Lite Beer, American traders are heroic, photogenic workaholics, stalking wealth for the public weal, watch them perish in their money-belts, ticker-tape shrouds, Stooges are out of there

What are you, a warrior or worrier?
Worrier. My wife's afraid of a warrior.
Is it appropriate to scrutinize an ethical activist's motives regarding violence when the vast, chronic, institutionalized violence goes unchecked, in fact accelerates?
(Pause)
Answer me. Is it?
I don't know.

in D.C. now, war mania, en route to the Pentagon for a briefing re their retention as super secret agents, striding abreast while whistling Yankee Doodle Dandy, meanwhile within the Pentagon, Big Boss, played by grandfatherly Charles Coburn, details the scheme: Stooges to be implanted in Himmler's inner circle, PORTENTOUS DISSOLVE, Stooges in SS livery, sucky jackboots, sexy helmets, goosestepping noisily in tandem through a marble corridor, presumably in Germany, Heil Hitlering, winding downward, suddenly in the bowel of an extermination-camp barracks, eyes-bones-stink, three-four to a bunk, asprawl, a stunned Curly stumbles, behind him Larry and Moe topple headlong, Kaboom! jackboots / buttocks / swastikas, DISSOLVE, vertical and at attention, the Stooges being debriefed in guttural Hollywood German by Nazi Uber-Boss Himmler, played with monocled, consummate smarminess by Conrad Veidt, can he convince our guys, with seductive appeals to heroic profits and pliant, golden Valkyries, to become *double* agents, no way, not in America / the movie, GRADUAL DISSOLVE, in this frame the boys are highstepping, shuffling's more like it, done lost their steady gig, McCARTHY-TIME, Jews now have pigment, high-profile poor have pigment, everybody who's nobody got pigment, rhumba to it, except redbaiters, pro-haters, don't rhumba, don't have the loins for it, Stooges in stir, Yellow Mama, hard time, "It Cain't Happen Here," prison-garb, leg-irons, shuffling through the dingy, shit-eating hot, it's just Carolina folks, state-prison barracks, post-bellum (which war you talkin' 'bout?), film-noir shadows, dead-weary limbs, dark listless forms in the narrow bunks, loud night insects, muted other sound, though, from somewhere, harmonica

Harmonica?
Yes.
What is it playing?
"We Weary of Dyin', We Aim To Make You Dead Instead."
Blues?
No.

ILLEGAL ALIENS

Anesthetic

I DON'T BRAKE FOR ILLEGAL ALIENS, the bumper-sticker read. Late-model Mercedes sedan, silver-grey, parked in the suburban shopping-mall. Bourgeois cradled the nail file in his left hand and, moving deliberately, made a nasty irregular scratch the length of the car, back to front.

Bondage

The reptile handler at the acclaimed zoo was holding a 22-inch, 16-ounce gila monster upside down in each hand, when one of the creatures twisted around and bit him, clamping down on his hand for about forty seconds. The handler was holding the gila monsters upside down in preparation for an anal probing with an "otoscope" to determine their sex. The examination was necessary because, as the curator of reptiles explained: "If you just look at them, you can't tell the girls from the boys."

Circus

Selected border crossings now retain medical technicians who operate sigmoidoscopes, a contraption inserted into the colon then viewed. Called sigmoidoscope because its S-shape permits entry around the sigmoid-shaped bend in the colon. Cocaine especially has been smuggled into the U.S. via this route, high, high in the courier's bung. According to federal drug-enforcement officials in the U.S., the "scope" has made a "tremendous difference."

Anesthetic

I'D RATHER BE BUTTING HEADS, the bumper-sticker said. Late seventies G.M.C. long-bed pickup, jacked up high on big tires, lumpen-suburban-macho style. Parked in the street. Bourgeois cradled the nail file in his left hand, and as he walked past on the sidewalk side, made a nasty irregular scratch the length of the car, back to front.

Bondage

The reptile handler was rushed to "Poison Emergency" of Misericordia Hospital where his condition was listed as "serious but stable." The gila's venom is not "injected" as with other reptiles, but seeps via the short furrowed teeth into the bite. Its jaws are exceedingly strong and it will clamp onto its victim, all the while grinding its teeth, for up to thirty minutes, ample time for a lethal dose to seep. However, since the gila is not a "totally irascible" species, according to the curator, its bite is "painful, hazardous, but not often fatal."

Circus

Less stuff going down at the borders. Because of the sigmoidoscope, the specter of the sigmoidoscope, the imago of the sigmoidoscope. Then where the hell does it come from— drugs? How come all the brothers in the NBA and NFL, in the major motherbleeping leagues, are getting busted for snorting, freebasing, crack-smoking, what have you? Getting busted, nothing! Brothers be dyin' from the shit. How they *getting* it if that damned sigmoidoscope doin' the job like you say, puttin' the bleeping fear of . . .

Anesthetic

I'm just joking. Bourgeois wouldn't do that to a G.M.C. pickup. Not to a G.M.C. pickup. Hell, pickup drivers (I'm not talking about slumming yuppies) can't help it. Work hard for bad pay, come home to their beer and grease, their TV, their aphasia. Besides, Bourgeois likes bumper-stickers, spread like that, ass-up like that, love-words, rage-words. And when Larry Holmes, then-heavyweight champ of the world, appeared at a benefit for a severely disabled fighter, the disabled guy, a Chicano, all messed up, said to the Media: "Yeah, he helped me, the champ—he put some stuff in my heart."

Bondage

But why wasn't the reptile handler wearing gloves? Well, "it's a question of how much safety you gain versus how much control you lose," the curator explained. "With gloves you lose your sense of touch, intimacy. For the gloves to be effective, they'd have to be thick as welding gloves. But then you can't feel a doggone thing."

Circus

Number 1: It ain't no individual courier just up from Bogotá with a couple-a-three cylinders of coke up his chute. Number 2: Unlike what some xenophobic U.S. senators claim, it ain't the soft-on-communism-south-of-the-border-banana-republics in semi-literate collusion against our virtue. Number 3: I hope you don't believe all that media jive about how many high-paid professional athlete brothers is using, because it ain't nothing but what like I said: media jive. Number 4: THE REAL DRUG IS IN OUR NOSE-HAIRS, IN OUR COFFEE, IN OUR BOUGHT GENITALS.

Anesthetic

May Day. Bourgeois among a busload of demonstrators. Off to D.C. The coalition sponsoring the march is emphatically multiracial, and Bourgeois' bus has Blacks, Hispanics, Orientals. Bourgeois himself (at the back of the bus) is white, middle-class, middle-weight, middling committed. Check that: Bourgeois is not terminally mediocre. He feels, he agonizes, atomizes, re-creates. He's re-created this passage which begins with "May Day." I want to be exact: *I've* created Bourgeois' re-creation. Or so it appears. Re-appears. Re-appears with variations. One cannot dunk one's foot into the same river twice. One cannot dunk one's *same* foot into different rivers twice. No river is unmediated. No unmediated river is . . . NOTE: This privileging of mediation / self-consciousness, often called "postmodern," is a luxury restricted to the "first world." Has nothing to do with the systematic *unmediated* extermination of South African Blacks.

Bondage
The gila monster *(Heloderma suspectum)* is indigenous to the deserts of Arizona and southeastern California. According to the glossy Arizona bi-monthly *The Sonoran Desert,* it is *not* true that once the gila monster bites "it doesn't let go until the sun goes down."

Circus
Thas right, we *alambristas.* But first of all we *vatos,* and *vatos tienen bolas,* man, big fuckin' *chiles.* If you think we gonna live like *gusanos* in T.J., you one shit-eating *pichon.**

Anesthetic
Bourgeois works (in his head) with the poor, the disaffected, helps them to get what's theirs. Bourgeois knows (in his head) where the key joints are, how to apply pressure. That earlier business about bushwhacking the Mercedes with his nail file is imagined, Bourgeois' lark, a nausea-video, what does it mean? you'll never read it in your history text, you'll never read about the dismal ruminations of the Mexican woman squatting in the dried-up river bed, between the Mexican bull-ring and the American helicopter base, waiting for night, will she / won't she get raped? She'll get snatched and bussed back, you'll never know what she felt.

Bondage
You hear about that patriot in Maryland, near D.C.? He wounded a dachsund with a crossbow. Then hacked it to death

---

Pachuco, or *Cholo,* slang, which, "translated," reads: "That's right, we're illegal aliens. But first of all we're dudes, and dudes have balls, man, big fucking dicks. If you think we're going to live like freeloaders in Tijuana, you're one shit-eating chump." *El Libro de Calo: Pachuco Slang Dictionary,* ed. Harry Polkinhorn, *et al.* (San Diego, 1983).

with his axe. Claimed the dachsund was harassing his German shepherd. Which is why zoos are good. They re-create a savage lifestyle for your citizens, display gila monsters for the unwild. Ergo the otoscope. Can't display 'um if you don't breed 'um. Like the ante-bellum plantation laird said: "We aim to re-create under conditions of captivity a natural environment."

Circus
There's San Ysidro, and thirty-five yards north, just over the border: the golden arches of *McDonalds*. The aliens will make their move between three-ten and three-twenty a.m., slink down the mesa, scurry across the dry river bed, scramble through the spiky brush, crawl through the drainpipe, emerge just a few yards south of *McDonalds'* parking lot. Unless they're spotted first in the *migras'* infrared scopes. These scopes register body heat, transform the darting low-to-the-ground aliens into luminous silhouettes of yellow-green body heat. Your greaser alien is hot, eats chilis for breakfast, has an unbridled temperament, is always horny, sleeps too much during the day and so is active at night, finds glitter irresistible, don't shave. Picking one up on the infrared scanner's about as easy as catching a fart in a glass.

Anesthetic
Between bushwhacking Mercedes and accusing History, Bourgeois is just like you or me, but for his exceptionally large ears. Watches sports on TV, goes to the zoo with his wife and kids, drives a G.M. car, doesn't not drink Coors, votes Republican / Democrat, thereby exercising his "freedom of choice," strikes out the side at night before sleep, scans the stockmarket data in the corporate newspaper at breakfast, is bullish on electronics, owns a family computer, is confidently certain that robotics and biospheres "are our future" with uncontaminated Science at the helm.

Bondage
Your gila is not a "totally irascible" species. Your Bantu neither. "Lethal injection," which made its debut in Texas

with the execution of Charlie Brooks, once a Bantu, is "more humane" than older, conventional procedures: hanging, garroting, firing squad, gas chamber, electric chair, guillotine, immolation. But hold off battening on your moral nausea for this query:

"A polity must have its circuses, agreed? Whom then would you display?"

"Why, I would display every living mom of every corporate vice-president under the age of fifty-three. I would display J. Pierpont Morgan's long thin admonishing forefinger and quivering wattle. I would display the lethal injection that injected the saline solution into Charlie Brooks' veins in Huntsville, Texas. I would display the video replay of PCBs poisoning the bloodstream of a five-year-old red-haired girl in Norwood, Massachusetts."

Circus

Hey, freedom of choice is what they *want,* and if it means being scoped or scanned or any damned thing else to get here to get this freedom of choice they'll put up with it no problem. They'd like to make history, why not, EX-GREASER HITS IT BIG, IS NUMBER 1. "My name is Jose Diaz. Pepito Diaz—put it that way. I'm Randy now, I got real small ears."

Anesthetic

I've oiled Bourgeois good, finessed him into this seam or that, he's no more a G.M.-car-family-man than Ralph Nader, the only floppy discs he owns are on his head, which don't make it better, since what he can't hear one way he hears another, I mean the braying of heifers under the branding irons of cowboys, the diamond chords of harp seals murdered in D major if the crop is fair, C major if it's doggone good like it should be if we prepare real well give it a hundred and ten percent suck it up from the gut show what we're made of live clean in the Disney we're number one the Dallas Cowboys AMERICA'S TEAM-missile . . . What would *you* do if you were me with a Bourgeois in your stomach?

Bondage

It's not a gila monster, it's a text. It's not a lethal injection, it's the hegemony of closure. In any case, the reptile handler is on the mend, look for him on any Saturday morning under the hood of his G.M.C. pickup. If one hand is free stick a Coors in it, if the other hand is free stick a wrench in it. What separates him from the men under him at the zoo is the music he likes: Hank Williams-era country rather than the new stuff, and once in a while Dixieland from *old* New Orleans. Does he like reptiles? Shoot yeah, he's grown to kind of like those suckers, been with them goin' on seventeen years now, it's a job, the pay ain't bad, I'll tell you something 'bout animals—they got their good points, things not even all humans have.

Circus

Sigmoidoscope reminds Bourgeois that Greek fraternal societies have made a "remarkable comeback" in American universities throughout the country. Ditto ROTC. Ditto workaholism. Ditto God. Ditto "pragmatism." As for drugs, take the Andean Indians: they sow but reap not, they perish at birth or before the age of forty, they're wedded to their thin-aired, unforgiving earth, and those suckers are *always* high on coca, chew it every doggone chance they get.

Anesthetic

Take Bourgeois. After his most recent nervous collapse he dreamt that his ears were small, that his floppy disc was between his thighs like it was supposed to be, that he was indisputably white and well-paid and white. That he drank Coors and vomited pearls, wherefrom his comely wife he bedecked. That he was impervious to words like sublate and reify and signifier and hermeneutic and postmodern—Never mind, forget this dumb conceit! Cancel the chain of dependent clauses that follows "nervous collapse." Check that—cancel *all* of it, the whole bleeping panel. Yeah, "take Bourgeois" and break both his kneecaps.

Bondage

"I'm mentally ill, hard of hearing and different." Zoos bring folks together. People with different politics, lifestyles and toilet habits will tolerate and even like each other a little watching the animals behind the cage, watching the cute caged animals. And with prudent doses of the appropriate pharmaceuticals a knowledgeable professional can almost transform the mentally ill individual into a numbed church-going admirer of caged animals like the rest of us.

Circus

Technocrats have proposed that a nuclear waste site be established in Southern California, specifically in the desert bordering Arizona, since the earmarked area would have to possess a low water table and little rainfall, so that the radioactive material would not "migrate." Meanwhile the *migras* drink beer and patrol the wide California-Mexico border and use their infrared scopes and joke about the greasers. Why joke about the greasers? Because the *migras* are underpaid and their wives hate Calexico and there's never enough beer and what happens is they nab the greaser, bus him back over the border, and the next a.m. he tries it again, and he don't quit trying until he makes it to the U.S., takes work for non-union shit wages, which naturally messes up the American worker who's used to a particular life-style that he don't want to do without, why should he?

Anesthetic

Confession: Bourgeois don't like people. Not in the flesh. Not without death. With death he likes them. Show them their death, strip them to bone, to fish. Bourgeois likes them okay with death, but not otherwise, what's to like? But then white folks, home-owners, zoo-lovers, don't go for Bourgeois, with his floppy discs and haunted eyes and female intuition. Have you ever seen a dude go zoo? Implode all over the damn place? That's Bourgeois' kind of people.

Bondage

I described the reptile handler as holding the gila monsters upside down, one in each hand, but don't get the wrong idea, this does not constitute mistreatment or anything of the sort, just as the nurse's slap on the rump of the newly-delivered infant does not constitute mistreatment. Item: Two recent scientifically controlled polls, with a margin of error of point six percent, have both concluded that, after the veterinarian, the zoo animal-handler is the most "widely respected animal professional in the U.S."

Circus

When the courier was apprehended with eighteen grams he couldn't believe it, kept shaking his head and grinning incredulously over the sigmoidoscope, that they'd actually stick that contraption in him to get eighteen lousy grams. He was still shaking his head but had stopped grinning when they slapped the cuffs on him. He said: "Shit, who don't like to get high?" I'll answer that: Charlton Heston don't like. Prime Minister Margaret Thatcher don't like. Edwin Meese The Third don't like. Mother Teresa don't like. The Buddhist martial leader of Burma don't like . . .

Anesthetic

What else? Bourgeois like this quotation from Brecht's *Galileo:* "It is clearly understood: he is not to be tortured. At the very most, he may be shown the instruments," for example sushi that wish you "bon appetit": minuscule Japanese-made (American-distributed) edible computer chips implanted in the salmon roe, which also inform you of traffic conditions, the pollution index, baseball scores, the closing Dow . . .

Bondage

Well they got the otoscope into the gila monsters' bungs and guess what? They were both girls. Which means another excursion to the Sonora Desert to capture at least one vigorous male that would breed with the zoo females. Which means they will have to sedate the captured gila and otoscope it *in situ.* This happens, and the first capture is a female. So are the second and the third. The zoo people capture eight gilas over five days and every one of them is female. They return to the zoo but then make a second excursion to the desert north of Tucson ten days later. This time they remain for nine days, during which time they capture eleven gila monsters—astonishingly, every one of the eleven is female, according to the otoscope. The three reptile-catchers are pissed and tired. One of them even questions whether the otoscope is a reliable gauge of gender, which provokes a fist-fight with one of the others who feels that the zoo's professionalism is being impugned. The third man breaks up the fight, but then that evening over chow it flares again and the zoo-defender stabs the otoscope-skeptic in the throat with his pocket knife. The skeptic dies almost at once and the assailant makes off on foot into the desert. The third man packs up the equipment and the eleven "female" gilas, contacts the police from his c.b., then contacts the chief reptile-handler at the zoo to say that he's coming home. Never makes it out of Tucson. Sideswiped by an eighteen-wheeler cargoing steer manure, the zoo-van crashes through an embankment, tumbles into a gully, catches fire, explodes. The driver is incinerated. The four cages with their eleven "female" gilas are jarred open and the creatures wamble off into the desert.

Circus

Didn't take them all that long—the greaser bigs in Mexico City, in Caracas, in Bogotá—to get wise to the sigmoidoscope. They notified their couriers: *Bung is out, forget the bung.* Instead the bigs had their physicians induce boils on the fleshiest portions of their couriers' thighs, secrete the grams under the boils, then when they got through to New York, L.A., Houston, Miami, lance the boils with a sterilized sharp instrument, recover the shit.

THIS IS YOUR AUTHOR SPEAKING:

Time now to zip this discourse up, impose coherence on it. You will have noticed that each of the three repeated sections was marked by *invasion:* A, property-defacement; B, otoscope; C, sigmoidoscope. Foregrounding this mechanical invasion, I've insinuated without much trouble its psychosocial concomitants, inscribed in the section heads themselves: **A**nesthetic, **B**ondage, **C**ircus.

I moved forward, backward, and, with Bourgeois' ruminations, laterally. Hectoring Bourgeois as he made his own hectoring observations on people and things has been a particular pleasure for me, the unmoved mover . . .

"Unmoved mover" is inaccurate; so is "coherence." I was being impious. Have a closer look, you'll see that "Illegal Aliens" has never stopped rupturing, refuses to be contained.

Try this: think of "Illegal Aliens" as a strain of Las Vegas, as described by the architect Venturi:

> Differences between the blazing outside and the cool, dark inside are poignantly strong, yet they are countercrossed by the domesticated "outside" inside the patio and by the night-sky lighting of the casino lounges. Day is negated inside the casinos, night is negated on the Strip . . . Beyond the town, the only transition between the Strip and the Mojave Desert is a zone of rusting beer cans.*

"Illegal Aliens" is a strain is a strain is a strain of Las Vegas.
Have a nice day / night.
Keep one eye on the encroaching desert.

---

*Robert Venturi, *et al.*, *Learning From Las Vegas* (The MIT Press, 1985, rev.).

HURRICANE CARTER

"Look for me in the whirlwind"
                    Marcus Garvey

TRIVIA TIME: What do Killer Bees, AIDS, Idi Amin, Pygmies and Nelson Mandela have in common?

Twenty years. I saw a quick shot of him on *Headline News* back to the camera walking through a Rahway State Prison corridor. Knees bent walking on the balls of his feet pridefully after all those years. I saw the strain. Still refusing their prison clothes job chow. Carter: "I happen to love my dignity better than I love my life. I let the administration know that if you are not prepared to kill me on the spot or maybe be killed yourselves don't put your hands on me." Friends brought him canned food/his wife gave up on him. Rubin Carter forty-eight years old contender before his lynching for the middleweight crown, Black

man. So how come Hurricane is the the news? After nearly twenty years Federal Judge H. Lee Sarokin reversed the triple murder conviction of Carter and John Artis citing deliberate withholding of evidence and cynical pandering to racism / the three victims drinking at the Lafayette Bar and Grill were white. Black Carter black Artis in a white car that "resembled" the gunmen's car had been picked up soon after the shooting *on the opposite side of Paterson.* How could they have gotten there so fast? Shoot! You know how Hurricane drives. "His bullet head is shaved and his beard and mustache look sinister. He wears white/violet/green/blue berets pulled at a rakish angle over his right ear iridescent suits pointed Italian shoes. In the ring glaring from under a monk-cowled robe as he listens to instructions from the referee Carter hopes to terrify his opponent *before* the fight." Quoted from a 1964 article in *The Saturday Evening Post* called "A Match Made in the Jungle" re Carter's upcoming fight with Joey Giardello for the middleweight crown.

Judge Sarokin said that Hurricane Carter should not spend another hour in prison. Which prompted *The New York Times* to unlock its word bank: in one of its patented "balanced" editorials, the *Times* commended Judge Lee Sarokin's opinion as "well-reasoned" while chiding him for his "excessive lecturing on the need for 'compassion.'"

TRIVIA ANSWER: They all hail from the depths of the Dark Continent.

The *Times:* "Judge Sarokin's ruling if upheld would let the prosecutors try both men again with whatever evidence remains untainted." Another trial? Untainted? After twenty years? Though one of the shot whites who later died said Carter and Artis *weren't* the killers. Though Carter and Artis "passed" a polygraph test. Though the only two witnesses two white men committing a burglary at the same time in a nearby metal company copped a plea "failed" a polygraph test / then after the five-year statute of limitations on perjury recanted their testimony insisting they were pressured into the damaging testimony by Paterson police detectives. Though a second trial was held after the recantation and Carter and Artis were found guilty again and Carter was re-sentenced to two life terms.

Dylan in his ballad "Hurricane" sees Carter as a Buddha isolated in his cell. A "terrible" Buddha as in the Tibetan pantheon silent under extreme compression for twenty years then the eruption. *What eruption?* In South Africa and around the globe following the death of Nelson Mandela sixty-eight years old imprisoned for twenty-three years black freedom-mongering his crime. In the chest at the not-guilty verdict arrived at by the all-white jury re the six police officers involved in the lynching of Michael Stewart caught inscribing a graffito in a subway on a filthy hot New York City night. In the chest at the lynching of a black teenager in Alabama in which a twenty-nine-year-old white chose a black at random cut his throat then hung him from a tree across from his (the white man's) house to demonstrate that the "Klan is bigger than ever in Alabama." A.D. 1985. Eruption in the chest and brain and body politic. Stepin

Fetchit died the other day. TV and newspapers in their brief obituaries gave his birthdate variously as 1895 1902 and 1909. Stepin Fetchit took his name from a horse he'd won some dollars on. Don't confuse him with Mantan Moreland both played Charlie Chan's entertainingly shiftless bug-eyed-at-the-drop-of-a-pin chauffeur black black. The old Charlie Chan flicks have recently made a comeback both Warner Oland's and Sidney Toler's versions of the phlegmatic inscrutable Oriental sleuth delivering Confucianisms while solving baffling crimes. Who here remembers that Charlie Chan was not a private detective was in fact attached to the Honolulu Police Force? Stepin Fetchit subsequently became a Muslim *Black* Muslim and in 1970 sued CBS for televising clips from his early caricature roles without his permission. Lost the suit. Became an adviser to Muhammad Ali. Ethel Waters who began her long career in vaudeville as Mama Stringbean is still best known as Beulah the comical generous-natured nay all-forgiving housemaid on network radio then TV. "Good communication is everything." (Lee Iacocca)

write / spoke
spook / white
hop / Hopi
prick / sphere
spine / fault

ladder / rupture
lethal injection / gas

Why did Hurricane Carter reject his Rahway State Prison "privileges"? Because any acknowledgement of his status would assume that he accepted his conviction. "I don't want movies tv radio. I don't go to the yard. I don't play." Jim Brown on the set of *The Dirty Dozen* 1967 with Lee Marvin/Bronson/ Cassavetes let the tossed football between shoots hit him on the chest fall to the ground he was he said finished with football/no lolly for Whitey.

CHRONOLOGY (adapted from *The NY Times*):

6.17.66: Two men and a woman shot to death at the Lafayette Bar and Grill in Paterson New Jersey.

10.14.66: Rubin (Hurricane) Carter and John Artis arrested and indicted for murder in the three killings.

5.27.67: A Paterson jury convicts Carter and Artis. Carter sentenced to two consecutive life terms Artis to one life term.

9.13.74: Alfred Bello and Arthur Bradley the only witnesses who identified Carter and Artis as the gunmen recant their testimony contend they were pressured by Paterson detectives to give false testimony.

3.17.76: New Jersey Supreme Court overturns the convictions ruling that the prosecution withheld evidence favorable to the defense. Both defendants released on bail.

12.22.76: At a second trial a Paterson jury finds Carter and Artis guilty. Carter again sentenced to two life terms Artis to one life term.

12.22.81: Artis released on parole after serving 15 years in prison.

8.17.82: The New Jersey Supreme Court in a 4-to-3 decision rejects an appeal for a new trial. Carter remains in prison.

11.7.85: Judge H. Lee Sarokin of Federal District Court in Newark overturns the second convictions after finding that the prosecution committed "grave constitutional violations" at the second trial. Hurricane Carter freed pending a decision re a third trial. Hurricane Carter/a pending freedman.

—I look at Hurricane I think of what's his face? The middleweight champ? Marvelous Marvin Hagler. Both black middleweights with shaved heads. I never understood the shaved head deal. Guess it makes you look shit-eating. Didn't Hurricane knock out a quarter horse? Left hook is what I heard. Right before his fight with Giardello in '64. You know how the purse for that fight was divided? $102,500 for Giardello, $12,500 for Carter. They say the Mafia was running the show they don't like black folks. Besides Hurricane had already done ten in the joint. He needed a big fight too bad he lost. He was you know a stutterer when he was young learned real fast to "speak" with his fists. Earlier you mentioned that African— Mandela. Was he a boxer? He was a chief or something wasn't he? You didn't happen to catch *Miami Vice* last night? All about Hemingway and stuff. Phil Collins the rock star played a drug pusher. Feckless charming. Rod Steiger in a tight black wig did a cameo as Kadafi. The Libya guy? Don't smile it may be the only politically liberal show on TV. *Miami Vice*. Accuracy in Media is eating their heart out. So how you doin'? I'd like to close this installment of my word bank with the following. Where do we go from here? I say Rock and Roll constituted as it mostly is by street kids black and white raising millions for famine relief in Africa. Don't say it I know. Famine relief has already been reconstituted into acne relief/beer-thirst relief like them fetches top dollar. While starving AIDS-inflicted black Africa has been parasitized. Not by Marxism as we're sometimes told. By top-dollar sentimental contaminated largesse which is conveniently mistaken for social practice. Result: the good poor the real victims the truly deserving are baptized in new formula Coke more sweetener less carbonation. "Americans give more to charity than any other two countries in the world." (Ed Meese) They're all of them louts don't underestimate them. Remember young Adolph. Have a good one.

MORE TRIVIA: "You have failed to establish that a bona fide marital relationship can exist between two faggots." Who said this?

Likely the police decided to frame bad-ass Hurricane only *after* they picked him up. John Artis the cops didn't give a crap about one way or the other. Artis just in the wrong place at the wrong time/his ass.

"AIDS is believed to have leapt to America when thousands of Haitian exiles moved from Zaire to the States in the mid-Seventies. Many of them turned to male prostitution to survive financially." Does Idi Amin have AIDS? An interesting question and one that is increasingly being asked in august government caucuses throughout the First World. Would anyone care to estimate how many progeny Amin sired via his hundred-odd "wives"? And if as now seems likely Amin was a carrier who was not himself at risk did he *know* that he was a carrier? Did he sire his vast progeny with the knowledge that he was a carrier? Perhaps most intriguingly was Amin acting under the authority of a foreign power?

Called "Hurricane" because it's good PR for every boxer to have a flashy monicker. Because as the *Post* article puts it he "was a kind of schoolboy Mount Vesuvius at age 11 sent to Jamesburg for atrocious assault" who as a welter- then middleweight wrecked Fernandez and Griffith and Dick Tiger. Because Rubin you've noted ain't no Rocky or Sugar or Gentleman Floyd. How about all the problems Jim Brown's been having best fullback to come down the pike/rape and shit he's nearly fifty now coming on like he's twenty and stud buck of the West. How about this new one Bo Jackson played football down there in Alabama/Auburn. "Look at his dang back. His back is as broad as a dang bull." Bo's white coach name of Dye said that only one problem Coach went on to say and that's Bo's "attitude" do he *come to play* every day?

TRIVIA ANSWER: The INS (Immigration and Naturalization Service) in its "official" response denying a homosexual Australian immigrant resident status.

Hurricane Carter referring to a killing of a black tavern owner by a white man in Paterson two nights before the crime for which he was imprisoned: "White man told the police 'Yeah I killed the nigger but I was insane that night.' So the court finds him guilty of second degree murder and gives him 25 to 30. After serving three years he's freed so that if he gets insane again he can kill him another nigger. John Artis and I who said we have nothing to do with this/there's no evidence that can connect us with this/we get triple life."

The dominant ideology marginalizes working-class blacks and gays and women because they are central, crucial to profit-making and political power. The dominant ideology institutionalizes the "avant-garde" because it is hamstrung, marginal.

Mae Thelma Carter after Rubin had served nearly ten years before (how long can a body wait?) she divorced him: "I never had a moment's doubt that my husband did not commit the crime. Rubin is not a lying man."

Dylan now counted among the institutionally avant-garde as evidenced by my skirting around quoting him can't afford it / in his ballad "Hurricane" wonders how such an estimable man can have his life manipulated by louts. Shoot Carter's a better man now than what he was twenty years ago when we nabbed him for the triple homicide what do you say to that? You know what he said in '64 about the ten years he spent in prison before this latest twenty? "If I didn't go to prison I'd be dead. Somebody would have killed me or I'd have killed somebody the way I was living" according to *The Saturday Evening Post*. Lookit between channeling his aggression into boxing and copping his ass in prison for thirty of his forty-eight years we saved ourselves a shitload of grief and if it's up to the Passaic County Prosecutor Carter's not home free yet not by a long shot don't matter what your Jew liberal federal judge pulls out of his drawers.

bitch / stud

breathe / count
lynch / text
Cancer / Cancer

FINAL TRIVIA: If one man up against it took what Hurricane Carter took for all those isolated years and didn't go zoo / what's gonna happen when all us living cells resolve to go zoo together?

TWO

TONTO

FIRST SPEAKER: Their sufferings are enormous.
SECOND SPEAKER: It is not enough to suffer.

Lenny Bruce mock stentorian: ARE YOU TONTO THE IN-
DIAN? Well, I'm your executioner, just kidding, big
reservation you've got here, Tonto, twenty thousand acres
stretching out to the border, and all your own shit, you're
sovereign, right, reparation for genocide from your, our, every
mother's son's breakfast cereal, cruddy land though, badlands,
arid as all get out, great terrain to get buried in, how would you
like to put chow in your belly, put your people to work, make
some steady green for the reservation, no I'm not talking
bingo, bingo won't make you snot, you ever hear of PCBs,
toxic waste, I reckon you're wonderin' what all I've got in my
britches, I've got a wad that won't quit, all you do is lease me a
hundred acres, I pay you fifty thou up front, plus twenty-five
thou a year, plus steady work for fifty of your braves at six
dollars an hour, which'll keep gas in their pickups, keep them
gassed up too, I could care less, your lifestyle is your own
damn business, I'm talking dollars for services rendered, like
what you did on your pony Scout in full gallop at the side of,
and slightly behind, the magnanimous mythic masked man
with his long pistol astride Silver his white-on-white stallion,
Lear had his fool, but hey it's Super Bowl weekend at the
Superdome, Super Bowl XX, big big stakes, you want history:
your Aztecs beheaded the losing captain (like now), your
Mayans beheaded the winning captain (moony wimps), the
ball represented the sun (before Xerox), the seven players
represented the planets, the "fans" witnessed the warrior's
execution, dark-skinned warrior executed (like now), TV cam-

era in the kill-room in the Georgia prison, "brought to you by . . ." dollars for prayer, Super Bowl Shuffle, you know we polled you reservation folks by phone, those of you had phones, sampling error of plus or minus six percent, asked whether you'd accept steady bucks for toxic waste, you all said you would, no problem, well, do you want to stroke my wad, think of it as your strategic defense initiative, popularly known as Star Wars, Navaho against Hopi, with Bronson as the Navaho and, say, Brando as the Hopi, pensive, moody, but white goods underneath, you follow, hey it's the real world out there, finger your stick, seek out the sucker, substitute dynamite for sausage on the cartoon dog's plate, guess who the dog is, but think of it this way, it sure as shit beats starving, stumbling into a gully, then drowning in a flash flood, or choking on drunk vomit, totaling your pickup, or hanging yourself, I hear suicide is way up on the reservations, Indians like allegory, right, consider the hermit crab, it has no shell of its own, it seeks out a deserted mollusk shell, squirms into it, if sea anemones or other parasites affix to the shell so much the better, that's not the sun that's Xerox, great news what I heard about your boss, Yum Kak, pronounced "Kash", Maya God, generated humankind with his tears, I mean Clayton Moore a.k.a. the Lone Ranger, finally got permission to wear his mask into perpetuity, also his guns, heart-warming story, astride Silver, Tonto, how well did you *really* know him, scratch that, I'm talking bottom line, Injun, PCBs, toxic waste, don't believe all you see in the left-leaning, Zionist-polluted media, it's not *that* toxic, unless you come in contact with it, we've got to dispose of it, right, can't just leave it around where there are kids and such, you follow, we aim to bury it on your reservation, don't tell me you don't need the bread, shoot we're only talking a hundred acres, you lease us a hundred acres, which is a piss in the desert, we'll put your warriors to work, get drunk, drive their pickups, watch the Super Bowl Shuffle, PBS had something on you all, Indians: complex and prideful, silent as Japs in a jungle, prone to fire-water, PCBs got a bad rap, I wouldn't shit you, there are degrees of toxicity, sponsored by Shell Oil, you came here via the Bering Strait, am I

right, the ancient arenas were built to echo: ball against pad-
dle, for the gods to hear, solemn shit, real mythic, well *our* bigs
underwrote the Super Bowl in the Superdome, New Orleans,
Bourbon Street, Network noose, drunk fun (no crack for
blackie), hoo ha, Esso becomes Exxon, note the double
crosses, almost prone, *Kyrie* etcetera, my shiny corporate Mercedes drives into your reservation like the conquistador's sun-
like armor into Mexico, like the plantation laird's pious white
thunder in his britches, those are *your* mama's thighs, wise up,
bend down, Tonto

THE MARX BROTHER

Turn in your Mum

I asked him to point me to Highgate Cemetery and the old Brit was very nice about it, walking with me, several times addressing me as "guv." He left me about halfway and cut to Highgate High Street and "me pub." He pointed: "Carry on right, guv, about five hundred meters."

The two elderly ladies at the cemetery entrance took one look at me and pointed down what turned out to be the well-footed path to Marx, the ladies easily assuming that I wasn't there to visit the tomb of George Eliot, say, or Christina Rossetti. I was mildly offended. Why couldn't a preoccupied-seeming, salt-and-pepper-bearded intellectual be interested in Marx *and* George Eliot? I ought to pass on to them the marxist-feminist deconstruction of *Daniel Deronda* I read in a recent *New Left Review.*

Just joking.

If the old ladies assumed otherwise we wouldn't be inhabiting Foucault's contextualized universe, would we?

What I mean is . . .

I feel fey.

Summer in the U.K. Rain, rain.

Summer-punk girls in their high-top sneakers (oddly sexy), misalliance of tight pants or brief skirts and T-shirts, bra-less, inventive hair lunacy.

Ice Age, Stone Age, Bronze Age, Hey nonny, nonny,

Thatcher-Era England-O.

Visiting Marx's tomb in Highgate Cemetery.

Weeping birch, ash, holly, blossoming lime *(Tilia europaea).*

I'd rather be in bed with my wife (but you've had a row and you're pissed with each other. That's why you're in Highgate Cemetery alone, remember?).

Turn in your Dad

In Hampstead, near where Orwell worked in a bookstore, is a movie theater where last night we saw a pandering pop-film by Peter Weir, *Witness,* in which an Amish boy with big eyes, in emphatic Amish garb, witnesses a murder in a railroad men's room: blackman killer with his switchblade coolly, brutally dispatching white cop. Weir, Australian, previously known for his sentimental and slyly racist films about Aboriginals. Here the Philadelphia white detective, captain-rank, keeps a black weak-chinned sidekick, sergeant-rank, who, in a related incident soon after the first murder, is lynched. Meanwhile investigating white dick falls for Amish boy's radiantly sexy Amish mother. Wild shootup at the end in travelogue-pretty Amish country, black killer, a corrupted narc it turns out, gets it in spades, concluding with white dick compelled, after the sentimental American paradigm, to *not* hang them up, to go back solo to his tough-honest-cop-big-city "lifestyle." Hence radiant Amish mom lovelorn, little league Amish son doleful with big eyes, Dad-deprived. A single, non-consumable tableau remains in the memory bank: a purple martin (colonial nesting bird) house, in the sun-burnished high grass, overturned by a '68 VW Squareback /

Say No to Drugs

"PHILOSOPHERS HAVE ONLY INTERPRETED THE WORLD IN VARIOUS WAYS. THE POINT IS TO CHANGE IT."

Etched on Marx's tomb.

Imagine if you can Marx's unvandalized tomb in New York

or L.A. or Philadelphia, where they bombed MOVE.

Remember them?

They made noise on their loudspeakers, were behind in paying their utility bills, their children looked unkempt, they kept cats and dogs, had all changed their surnames to "Africa," hence the Philadelphia police dropped a bomb on the "bunker" on top of their house, other houses caught fire, the Fire Department refused to fight the fires, result: eleven people including four children killed, 253 people homeless, all black, the problem, we're given to understand, was Goode, the black mayor /

Biospheres with Slot Machines

Marigolds and lilies strewn on Marx's tomb, which, by the way, is on "unconsecrated" ground, not because Marx was Marxist, but because he was a Jew.

Actually the tomb was moved from another unconsecrated part of the cemetery in 1956 (according to the one-pound-fifty brochure called *Friends of Highgate Cemetery*). Were his earthly remains moved as well? Doubtful.

I find out later that Marx's tomb both in its old and new setting was and is periodically vandalized.

Change it.

The Philadelphia dick in Weir's *Witness* is Harrison Ford, whose skull resembles Bogart's, whose body and gait resemble Paul Newman in *Harper,* whose disjointed intensity resembles early Widmark, Alexander Godunov, the exiled Soviet ballet star, does a turn as the Amish rival for the stunning Amish mother, Kelly McGillis, a cross between young Grace Kelly and Margaux Hemingway, the black killer narc, very dark, resembles Brock Peters in *The Pawnbroker,* but walks like Jim Brown after getting up from a gang-tackle, bury Marx / bomb MOVE / Change it /

Turn in your Mum

"I am not going to dignify that question with a response. Except to say: our position is: we want the democratic process to work." To that end the Transportation Department has granted "mission approval" for the plans of a fledgling rocket company to carry cremated human remains into space in late '87 or early '88, it was announced on Monday. Space Services Inc. of Houston, Texas, will use its own "small Conestoga Rocket" to transport the ashes of more than 10,000 humans into a 1900-mile-high orbit. Burial in space will start at $5900, a company spokesperson said.

Force-Move the Navaho

Centered atop the tomb: Marx's massive stone bust, looking like Walt Whitman-as-a-major-league-home-plate-umpire: the broad forehead, penetrating no-nonsense eyes, a hint of Asiatic craftiness about the eyes (the "structural" middle period rather than the "humanist" early period).

Two Japanese tourists in business suits pause to snap photos with Marx as a backdrop, move on.

(Japanese considered "honorary whites" in white South Africa.)

Buddhist adage: "If the wrong man uses the right means, the right means work in the wrong way."

A young British woman, very shy-looking, admires the tomb from ten feet behind me, virtually in the brambles.

> If you lived in Texas, Lady,
> That shyness were a crime.

A youngish black couple with their two children pass through without looking up. They set a wreath on a small stone twenty-five meters away (still unconsecrated ground).

A wren *(Troglodytes troglodytes)* skitters through the copse behind Marx's tomb, into the copse on the other side.

Proustian fragrance of blossoming privet.

A teenage couple in punk, her hand on his rump, amble across the path in the direction of the gate. If they knew Marx was here, they might want to make defiant love on or near his tomb, if they knew who he was, if they knew who they were.

Change it. How? Random urine testing.

The Ethnic Joke is Back

The wife and I still not liking each other. Meanwhile reading *Conversations with Claude Lévi-Strauss* and a "police procedural" by Wahloo and Sjowall. Grim inspector Beck, alternately cynical and socialist, in grimy Stockholm, not liking his wife, not carrying a gun. Elgar's "Enigma Variations" on BBC 3.

Turn in Your Dad

Day's writing done. What should I do with my erection? Visit Marx again? Righto. Hence walking down Swain's Way when I'm nearly run over by a scowling sod in an English Ford, the speeding car skirting the curb. Could be he divined I was en route to K.M. in Highgate Cemetery and wanted to save me the bother. Could be he's not British at all but from Texas and infected with the broad gesture and goin'-where-I'm-goin'-no-bullshit. Texas fetching mega-pounds in the U.K. these days, with the BBC and a commercial network in a vituperative bidding war for *Dallas* reruns.

Now if I were in a police procedural, getting run down by a sod in a Ford as I wended toward dead Marx would be all in a day's work, agreed? I twist off a bit of cypress, mash it with my fingers, sniff it while walking. I whistle off-key something from Schubert, who wore spectacles and died of syphilis, a good German like Marx; better, since he is buried in "consecrated" ground.

Fact: Schubert was Austro-German not German-German.

Fact: I'd feel surer writing this than living it.

Do you write for yourself?

I wouldn't say that.

For whom do you write?

For the reader who likes trees close together and people far apart.

(Pause)

Whom do you particularly admire among your contemporaries?

The Big Spit

So much for praxis.

Isn't writing praxis?

"At all time and in all places, the only social reality accompanying writing was the appearance of divisions and cleavages corresponding to caste or class systems. Writing seems to have been a means whereby men were reduced to a state of bondage by other men, a means of governing men and gaining possession of material things."

The eminent Lévi-Strauss said that.

But isn't he a Jew?

School Prayer in your Biosphere

Just two days ago I was the tall dark man in one brown shoe and we were playing bondage.

"Playing" in the sense of simulating. We're middle-aged.

As Lévi-Strauss persuasively puts it, Cubism (read: Postmodernism) appropriates the "primitive" without in any way embodying it.

"Real" bondage? Well, as you know, our President is in hospital, post-operative, healing rapidly, for his age, that's been well documented, he's a great, great healer, and while on the mend, less several feet of contaminated gut, he's apt to leaf through magazines, or read, scratch that, re-read, Zane Grey, or watch old movies, his own, say, or Bogart's, all the while "the single most important symbol, of his potency, remains a few feet from his bedside, at the Bethesda Naval Hospital, the black briefcase which can unleash the destruction of the planet, called the *football,* the briefcase contains 'authentication codes,' changed every day, which prove to the Secretary of Defense, and American military commanders round the world, that the man on the phone, instructing them to prepare, for nuclear hostilities, really is the President, of the United States."

Head-Butting at the Highest Levels

Prehensile Marx, all day long at his table in the British Museum. Headstrong, hemorrhoidal, humanist in his early period. Young Edward G. Robinson for this early period? No, Paul Muni. The Muni who did Benito Juarez. What about Ben Kingsley? He was smashing as Gandhi. Well, that's a thought. What about Burton? No, Burton is Trotsky, remember? Harrison Ford as Richard Burton as Trotsky? What about Katy Jurado as his paramour? No, that's Trotsky again. Well, what about the Jewish Ruth Roman as the patient, put-upon wife? Now you're thinking of Freud. In any case Marx was wedded to his vision.

We talking movie or docu-drama?

Meltdown

The British have an odd way of lying about the grass, mini-garbed, gathering up the precious sun in this wet, cold, Thatcherite summer, their bodies beige and contorted, recumbent all about Hampstead Heath and Waterlow Park, adjacent to Highgate Cemetery.

A middle-aged Scotswoman asks the elderly lady at the gate whether that handsome tree en route to Marx's tomb is a weeping beech. The woman responds: "I believe it is a weeping willow."

Fact: It is a weeping birch *(Betula pendula),* lamentably short-lived, susceptible of fungus.

Turn in your Mum

The orbiting container transporting the cremated human

remains (from Houston, Texas to outer space) would be coated with a highly reflective surface to make it easy to spot from the ground through small telescopes. The Transportation Department, which has authority to oversee commercial space activities, said it issued permission to proceed after consulting with the State Department, the National Aeronautics and Space Administration and the Department of Defense.

"But what about Star Wars? Won't this interfere with Star Wars?"

Indulgent smile. "Shoot. That's like saying, there's a McDonalds down there in Atlanta. Won't that interfere with a Burger King going up in Milwaukee? Outer space is a heckuva big area and one thing doesn't have to do with the other."

"Thank you, Mr. Secretary."

Moral Values Making Comeback

"Houston reminds me of *Dallas* which naturally reminds me of *Dynasty* and the Rock Hudson thing."

"All right."

"If the sturdy, handsome, affable, long-time Hollywood superstar can have contracted AIDS, it is time for the rest of us to realize there are homos in every walk of life. What I mean is, it is time to realize that AIDS is a problem of major proportions."

"All right."

"Why though did he have to fly to Paris, France for treatment? Hire that 747 like he did? I know for a fact that American technology is light-years ahead of the French socialists, and American hospitals are in the forefront of AIDS research."

(No response)

"You know what? Lot of folks were pissed that Hudson continued smooching American actresses on *Dynasty* even though he knew he had AIDS and how contagious it was."

"He was too scared to come out of the closet."

"President Reagan put the cap on it when he wired his best wishes to Rock sick as hell in Paris. The President's response in effect told the American people that it was high time we take AIDS *out* of the closet, that we begin to take it as seriously as, say, Legionnaire's Disease."

Tonight at the Everyman in Hampstead, Jules Dassin's 1947 "noir," *Brute Force,* with Burt Lancaster and Hume Cronyn. From the notes: "An isolated prison ruled by a sadist is a microcosm of the world as a meaningless hell. The only order is devoted to the total dehumanization of the inmates, which understandably becomes the inspiration for escape. But the way out is just as brutal and perhaps just as meaningless . . . A landmark movie that still shocks."

We were planning on catching this film (which I first saw as a child in the Bronx, before the "coloreds" moved in, though the resident whites were already worrying about it).

We had checked *Brute Force* off on the calendar a few days after we got to London. That was when we liked each other. Seems like a long time ago. Then again, tension is praxis. Like Marx of the early humanist period. Like Gramsci in prison. Like Hume Cronyn in *Brute Force.* Like Jerry Africa of MOVE. Like the Mahler who "withdrew his libido" in order to write *Kindertotenlieder.* Like the resplendent short-lived weeping birch attacked by fungus.

Cyanide in your Pharmaceuticals

If only I were somewhere else.

If only I were someone else.

Lafcadio Hearn, say. Vagabond-Buddhist. Born on my birthday. A century before.

A hump, a dump, and a drug.

Don't be shy / Give me all of your megahertz.

Last year at this time I visited Van Gogh at Arles. That "simple bonze."

He fell violently asleep.

Last year at this time I was still plotting my narratives.

Godard in *Passion* equates plotting and money-making. Godard among the first to film workers in their workplace.

Raymond Williams: "The central case in all matters of culture is that the lives of the great majority of people have been, and still are, almost wholly disregarded by 'history' as well as the arts."

Turn in your Dad

As I write at my window I watch the old lady in her thick rayon stockings, lit fag in her mouth, her tortoise-shell cat following her as she prunes her roses. One sees how the British withstood the Blitz.

"Ivy, another Victorian plant with funeral associations, is widespread in the Cemetery. It has the visual advantage of softening and knitting together the numerous memorials; and the ecological one of providing a refuge for wildlife in winter, food for insects, and nesting sites for birds. It is proposed to clear it only when covering historically or sculpturally interesting monuments." From *Friends of Highgate*.

Also: "Recent developments of blocks of flats in Highgate New Town are visually intrusive and should be screened by new tree planting."

Accommodate the "wild life" while segregating the domesticated poor who live in their "blocks of flats."

Why not accommodate the birds *and* the poor?

Never happen.

Why not?

The Big Spit

In the U.S. meanwhile Marxism has become telegenic.

A number of the most celebrated theoreticians have been offered enormous salaries to profess at unlikely universities, in North Carolina, in Texas. Profess what?

The invasion of the ideology snatchers.

Hold on: the University has a responsibility to the Zeitgeist. Which translates into periodically re-inventorying its conceptual arsenal.

Hence the institutionalization of the avant-garde.

Hence the new old complicity.

Nazi Youth

"Daniel Ortega is a swine," asserted Rep. Clint Petty (D-Ark.), another recent convert to the Contras' cause.

"Why do you say that, Congressman?"

"They—the Democratic so-called leadership—assured me last April that Ortega would do right if we gave him our vote. He didn't do right."

"What did he do wrong, Congressman?"

"He went to Soviet Russia is what he done."

Colored Poor Breed Poverty

Chomsky reminds us that it is precisely the smaller revolting countries, like Grenada, El Salvador, and Nicaragua, that are dangerous because they provide the other oppressed countries the most dramatic success against oppression.

Thus I would like to encourage in you, my audience, a "complex seeing." First, though, we've got to change it.

Change what?

(Pause)

I've lost my train of thought.

U.K., 6.85
U.S., 10.86, 7.87

BOMB

"Create unacceptable images"

So. Removing your glasses you lie on your back on the Kashmiri rug. Dakota, her dense purple hair reaching nearly to her *bleep,* undoes her frock, it slides to the floor. Pliantly, her back to your face, she straddles your smooth chest, stroking your slim long *bleep* with her long slim fingers. When you are swollen (imperially swollen) she removes the purple and gold scarf she wears as a halter (her *bleep,* surprisingly opulent on her delicate trunk, spring free). She slips the scarf round the shaft of your *bleep* and knots it. Then She dips the two longest fingers of her left hand into a filigreed jar and dabs the oily aromatic substance on her aroused pink *bleep.* Arching her back she positions her radiant *bleep* on your sleek face. While addressing her tongue to your *bleep,* she pulls the ends of the scarf tight, pulling, then releasing as your distended (martially distended) *bleep* discharges its *bleep* in

ceci n'est pas
pornographie

this is not

pornography, it
is a nuclear

holocaust, sim-
ulated of course, ac-
cording to an unim-
peachable source (the
wall

street journal):
"the reagan admin-
istration is moving
fast, on the airwaves,

off, to counter any
political fallout
from last night's
showing of abc-tv's
fictionalized account
of a nuke

nuclear holocaust:
'the day after,' wide-
ly publicized by abc
in part

in large part because
it was showing during
a four-week period in
which the two princi-
pal rating services
measure the networks'
viewing audiences in
major markets: a strong
showing in the ratings
war

war

translates into more
advertising revenue
for a network, the
movie, which depicts
the destruction of
lawrence, kansas

her face and on her *bleep,* at
which juncture *she* commences to
implode, grinding her *bleep* in
your face. It is a dance; you
call it "graceful degradation."
You have taught variations of the
dance to this girl and to other
girls. You are a populist / a
prince. You have enormous zest.
So.

From your supple, tawed
chamois, monogrammed utility case,
you withdraw a plaited rawhide
thong and then a monocle. You
remove your necktie, lie on the
bed, sleep on your back, dreamless-
ly. You sleep as Georgia opens
the door to your suite. She (her
cornsilk hair upswept) stands in
her silk magenta art-deco sheath
with its padded shoulders, one
hand on her hip, long back arched,
feet turned elegantly out, watching
you sleep. Extending her long
arms behind her neck, she undoes
the zipper, silk rustles to the
floor. The luminous striations
about her buttocks resemble the
sky over Alamagordo. Her patent
leather, platform-heeled pumps
which strap about her ankles she
does not remove. Carefully, she
removes your glasses, sets them
on a table; then straddling you,
she settles her scented *bleep* on
your sleek white face.

But now Georgia and
a young black girl lie on the low
wide bed, Georgia (but for her
platform pumps) naked, the other
wearing just a navel-length yellow

bleeding kansas, of-
fers no strategy for
avoiding a nu-

clear war, but (still
quoting the wall street
journal) it has ignited
a real-life political
battle, the

white house, after long
discussions about how
to react to the movie

movie, launched a cam-
paign to show that mr.
reagan is pushing for
arms control while the
soviets

while them soviets are
blocking such efforts,
democrats, meanwhile,
have seized

the initiative, invo-
king the movie to pro-
mote the impression that
mr. reagan is trigger-
happy, not

truly interested in
arms control, 'the day
after' (still quoting
the wall street journal)
comes amid rising tensions
and concerns over nuclear
war as the u.

s. begins deploying new
intermediate missiles in
western europe, although
the deployment was approved
by nato, demonstrators

T-shirt with NIKE in black sten-
cilled across the breast. The
girl is on her back, Georgia's
head nestled in the girl's scented
thighs. Georgia's fecund hair
across the girl's belly is like a
delta on black rich soil after
rain. Like an oil spill on an
estuary of the River Niger. You
go into the bathroom and *bleep*
long and loud in the toilet. You
run a bath. You lie in your
bath reading Evans-Wentz on the
Bardo Thodol (in an edited, illustrated edition put out by Time-Life
Books). The girl and Georgia come
into the barthroom. The girl has
just settled herself on the toilet
when you signal her to cease. "Over
here." She stands, comes to you.
You step out of your bath, your
bleep a salted weapon, a smart
bomb, a missile in its silo—about
to lift off. "Get into the tub,
Georgia." Georgia, pumps on, does.
You tell the girl: "Squat over her
bleep." Georgia grins, the black
girl is blank-faced; straddling
the tub she squats, her back to
Georgia. She is a slim girl,
feral, cocoa rather than black,
with nimble hips / dexterous hips.
While Georgia strokes the insides
of the girl's lustrous thighs,
the girl *bleep* with a high-pitched
hissing squeal on Georgia's *bleep*
and neck. When the girl is done
you lift her onto the floor, you
say: "Georgia, fetch me the wig
and the bible, then get her ready."
You are (you must be)

in europe cite the recent
u.s. invasion of grena-
da and the incursions in-
to lebanon and

the occupation of hon-
duras and the arming
and training of the nica-
raguan contras as proof
that the reagan admin-
istration is bent

is bent on using military
solutions for diplomatic
problems, yesterday on
nbc's 'meet the press,'
k.

adelman, director of the
u.s. arms control
agency, contended that
there wasn't any anxiety
in the administration over
the effects of the movie,

he said that because
the prez is working
for arms control, 'it's
going to reinforce support
for

the president,' k.
adelman did concede,
however, that if the
movie makes viewers think

there are 'simple answers
like the nuclear freeze
or like unilateral dis-
armament, if they do that
it will be damaging' to
arms-control efforts (this
is not

ready, and on the last day of her
life Indiana awakes without premoni-
tion. The sun is one hour old in
the pastel sky. The mountains
are purple, the timber green,
each brushed by the young sun's
silver (this is not real wilder-
ness, we can "hear" the freeway).
Indiana, naked, lies in the lean-
to beneath a canvas blanket, on
her left: you, asleep on your back,
your sleek white face glowing
with sun. And beneath the blanket
on Indiana's other side Georgia
sleeps on her stomach, one long
slim leg exposed. Indiana lies
awake on her side thinking of the
bleep she feels for you, and
through you for all things. Silently
repeating the "hostile takeover bid
prayer" you granted her, Indiana
becomes inflamed, and with gentle
inquiring fingers commences to
stroke Georgia's *bleep*. While
doing this very nice thing, Indiana
backs into yourself, at the ready
of course. Georgia, not yet fully
awake, moans softly; she moves
closer to Indiana, then turns so
that they are in each other's
arms. They kiss tentatively, then
more searchingly, urgently. Behind
her, Indiana can feel you react,
she widens her legs, pushing her
bleep against you. The sky is
bluing. Georgia's head is now by
Indiana's *bleep* and vice versa;
you, yawning, take Indiana from behind, while Georgia, underneath,
tongues you, her. You call this
position "arms control," and Indiana

pornography), similarly,
r. perle, an assistant
defense sec., insisted
that the soviets are to
blame them

soviets because (still
quoting the wall street
journal) they repeatedly
have rebuffed u.s. peace
efforts, speaking on abc's

'this week with david
brinkley,' he said the
soviets have answered
u.s. arms-control initi-
atives by calling for 'zero

intermediate missiles for
us and several hundred
for them for them,'

as part of the effort
to counter any criticism
generated by the movie
(still quoting the wall
street journal), the white
house has distributed a
white

paper detailing its
ongoing efforts to reduce
nuclear stockpiling, never-
theless, prez candidate
mondale, sensing a rupture
in the reagan perimeter,
said he (fritz)

would begin referring
to 'the day after'

'the day after'

in campaign speeches,
fritz mondale asserted

favors it. On this occasion you add
a coda, strangling the girl with your
tattooed forearm as you explode your
bleep in her *bleep* and everywhere.

that despite its denials
the administration 'is,
repeat is,

real worried about the
movie

movie.' "

BUTTERFLY McQUEEN

"Four figures emerged from this preoccupation with sex, which mounted throughout the nineteenth century—four privileged objects of knowledge, which were also targets and anchorage points for ventures of knowledge: the hysterical woman, the masturbating child, the Malthusian couple, and the perverse adult."

Michel Foucault
The History of Sexuality

THE HYSTERICAL WOMAN

Butterfly McQueen—they took her man.*
Why?
Interrogation. They'll burst his eardrums. Work over his genitals. Manacle his hands between his legs then hoist him by his hands to a hook on a pole then spin him around and assault him.
Why? What did he do?
Long story. How about some more Foucault?
Not now.
(Pause)
Can you hear the music?
What is it?
"Strange Fruit." Billie Holiday.
You know what all this reminds me of?
Say it.
Fashion doyenne Diana Vreeland's observation that "pink is the navy blue of India."
You know what India reminds me of? The inscrutable east. Last night at the movies I heard a woman weep uncontrollably, then laugh, then weep, through the showing of Kurosawa's *Red Beard,* 1965. Toshiro Mifune with a red beard played the gruff, though eminently human, that is to say, Buddhist, physician in a shogunate-period clinic for the poor.
Is "eminently human" Buddhist?
No. You caught me. *Aberrantly* human is what I meant. It's a

fine, brave film. Kurosawa on compassion, just that.

No mediations? No coyness? No stalking-horse technique?

None. There's a scene toward the end where peasant women shout the name of a dying beggar-child into a well. CHOBO! CHO-BO! CHO-BO-OO!

Does the child die?

The child is saved.

(Pause)

Red Beard actually was the second feature. The featured feature was Woody Allen's *Purple Rose of Cairo.* Do you know this quote of Althusser's: "Ideology is a representation of the imaginary relationship of individuals to their real conditions of existence"?

Do I know that quote? No, I don't know that quote.

It applies to Woody Allen. His Manhattan deletes Blacks, and his Depression—*Purple Rose* is set during the Depression—sentimentalizes the poor while deleting the in-fact poor.

(Pause)

There's a lot of Pirandello shmaltz having to do with illusion and reality. One typical scene has the movie-within-the-movie's characters, each in turn, announce to the audience her/his desire to "star." Except for one character, the caricatured, liveried black maid, who keeps on delivering highballs, never addressing the audience. It's not that Woody Allen wants to dramatize her marginalization; no, for Woody her status is indisputable.

(Pause)

Which reminds me. Beulah, Aunt Jemima, Dilsey, Hattie, Prissy, Lottie in *Mildred Pierce,* Sibyl in Ophuls' *The Reckless Moment.* What is it about the image of a middle-aged, twinkle-eyed, clean-smelling, infinitely patient black housemaid that is so appealing to the white movie-viewing public?

You mean TV- and video-viewing public, don't you? This is 1986. What is so appealing? Well, she's clean.

All right.

And she's friendly. She sees your private doings and don't think the worst of you. On the contrary, she takes you for what you are, warts and all. She tucks your blond little baby in. Also

she represents seamless continuity because she endures.
(Pause)
Can I give you that quote by Foucault?
Might as well.
"It is an irony of history that the Hitlerite politics of sex remained an insignificant practice while the blood myth was transformed into the greatest blood bath in recent memory."

THE MASTURBATING CHILD

I remember this photo by the sports photographer Conlon of Lew Gehrig and Babe Ruth in their heyday. Gehrig, looking like a thicker-set Paul Newman, is gripping his bat at the handle and holding it out at a right angle from his waist while the Babe is admiringly fingering the bat's fat tip. Gehrig's expression is priceless: innocent, bemused, prideful but not cocky. The Babe looks duly impressed but a little ironic too—after all his is about as big.

Yeah, the Babe would booze and tomcat all night long then show up at the stadium the next day at noon and go three-for-four with two homers. Gehrig of course was just the opposite, honest as the day is long and a great family man.

Somebody ought to write a book about those guys who drink and tomcat all night then go out the next day and strut their stuff like professionals. I'm thinking of the Babe, Bobby Layne, Bo Belinsky, Broadway Joe Namath, Harry Greb the fighter, Leon Spinks. Call the book *Burning it at Three Ends* or something. Yeah, maybe they shorten their career by a couple years, but they sure as hell have fun in the meantime.

Hey, don't get me wrong. I'm talking honest booze not drugs—crack, speed, angel dust, pot, like what's going on in sports today. It's disgraceful, an insult to America's national past-time and a lousy role-model for today's youth. Commissioner Ueberroth is absolutely right with his plan to do mandatory drug testing on every player in the game, and knowledgeable fans and image-conscious players are 120 percent behind him. I read or heard some bleeding-heart say something about Ueberroth's plan being racist. Horsebleep! If you think that maintaining the standards of Gehrig and Ruth and Dimaggio and Hodges and Mantle and Koufax and Rose is racist then your butt don't belong here in the first place.

I heard someone else say that Ueberroth is a grandstander, that he has his eyes on the Republican nomination for Senator in California. The way I see it is he's no grandstander but he's ambitious like he should be since he's a man of enormous capabilities and a heroic money manager—look how much he saved us on the Olympics.

The first time I came I sprayed the ceiling no lie I was thirteen jacking off in the living room like I always did when all of a sudden I felt these crazy feelings real deep inside that wouldn't quit and then it happened a goddamned geyser I sprayed the whole room just about but what I remember is the ceiling I'm talking about your pre-war buildings ceilings fifteen feet high/or higher.

When it was clear that the L.A. Olympics were a huge success a TV reporter asked Peter Ueberroth who he wanted to play him when they made the made-for-TV movie of the L.A. Olympics. Ueberroth—one of the few times you'll catch him off-guard—blurted out: Rock Hudson. Of course this was before the tragedy of Rock Hudson having AIDS became common knowledge.

If you asked me I'd say someone like Van Heflin—to play Ueberroth—an actor of rock-hard integrity, not flashy but romantic in his way, and a good family man (do you remember him in *Shane?*), and no question of his sexual preferences, and a winner.

THE MALTHUSIAN COUPLE

For winning the double-dutch rope-jumping championship of "Harlem, U.S.A.," the four black adolescent girl winners got to visit London, England. One of them, Wilma-Mae Tompkins, 12-years-old, on her return to Harlem, talked about London: "It real nice / It old / It even smell different."

Colin Beresford (Oxon. '60), lives in Westminster and is an executive at Lloyd's Bank. Muriel Potter Beresford lives in Westminster and is an estate agent. For his work-a-day Colin Beresford dresses as you would expect. For weekend or bank holiday he wears tweeds and either an ascot or his school tie. He is sallow, rather tall and stooped, with hair the color of pale ale too long in the bottle, and he always looks as if he could stand a good wash. He tends to stride rather than walk. He is a Tory. So too is Mrs. Beresford. They are childless. By design not incapacity, as both Beresfords have had occasion to explain. Mrs. Beresford recently went into hospital for "minor" surgery and died on the operating table of "complications." Her age was forty-two. Colin Beresford was advised by his solicitor not to bring suit against the hospital. Beresford was dry-eyed at his wife's funeral, but an acquaintance confided that he broke down briefly the day after and referred feelingly to his wife as "a good old stick." Mrs. Beresford died on Friday, was interred in "consecrated ground" in Highgate Cemetery on Sunday, Colin Beresford returned to work at Lloyd's on Tuesday. (Yes, Beresford likes Elgar but he also likes Britten and of course Haydn. Vaughan Williams he can take or leave. He cannot stomach Delius.)

It is at this juncture that Colin Beresford changes his name to Lumumba, leaves his position at Lloyd's, moves to London's East End and does his part to organize the masses against the Tory oppression. That set into motion, he moves down to Brixton where he works with the disaffiliated blacks. From there he moves into an Indian-Pakistani enclave in southeast London, where, interposing his body between a gang of marauding skinheads and a Pakistani family, he is crowned by a brass knuckle, killed.

The foregoing is my invention. I modeled Beresford-Lumumba on George Orwell who partially liberated himself when he partially jettisoned the Eton-poisoned Eric Blair. This of course was before "morality" became a party game. Called "A Question of Scruples," the game was invented by Henry Makow, a Canadian. According to *The New York Times,* the game's "manufacturers are already comparing sales

of the product to those of Trivial Pursuit in its early days and
expect to sell a million copies by Christmas."

Foucault is unsurprised. He writes: "not only will you sub-
mit your sexuality to the law, but you will have no sexuality
except by subjecting yourself to the law."

THE PERVERSE ADULT

demanding jobs the blacks swept out of their bus yellow
school bus procured somehow and stormed the eastside construction site but were driven back into the street by the white
steel workers 25 or 30 of them from this site and from two
others on the plush eastside evidently someone had leaked

alerted the white workers from two nearby sites and several
wearing colorful baseball caps against the sun hustled over to
join the fray calling themselves black economic survival based
in the hunts point section of the south

bronx the demonstrators claimed they wanted jobs according
to a witness at the scene two of the demonstrators burst into
the brownstone office of the builder asking for jobs when told
there weren't any jobs for them they bolted leaped into the bus
and gears grinding hurtled five hundred meters east on 58th
street to the manville affiliate construction site but by the time
the blacks got there a contingent of steelworkers had arrived
and a second was on its way as recorded by the same eyewit-
ness eight or ten of these blacks immediately bunched into an
elevator shaft rode it to the roof 45 stories up where with this
wild glaze over their eyes they walked right out on the naked
steel girders screaming stop

the job stop the job all the while making menacing gestures at
four white welders eating their hero sandwiches according to
lieutenant ww of the 28th precinct the welders told the tres-
passing blacks to buzz off at this some of the trespassers
started to throw punches but the outnumbered welders were

able to hold their own until ten of their buddies brandishing baseball bats and steel fittings poured out of the shaft at the opposite end of the structure and confronted the blacks on the narrow steel beams 45 stories up it

was a miracle lieutenant ww said that none of our guys were killed in fact the trespassers were routed driven into the street where they were rounded up booked for criminal trespass attempted assault the contractor for the 45-story manville affiliate said i can't understand why they got so worked up these demonstrators our hiring average of minorities blacks hispanics you name

it is competitive with any construction firm in the northeast to be truthful with you this issue is history has no teeth in it could be these demonstrators had something else on their mind fact is in the last four months according to an internal security spokesperson who has closely monitored the situation the so called black economic survival has mounted protests at more than half a dozen construction sites on manhattan's choice eastside nor have they chosen randomly ibm xerox ma bell have been among the structures targeted by the demonstrators however today was the first time their pique erupted

into violence and now they're going to pay the price promised lieutenant ww there are channels you know and you got to play by the rules or get off the pot besides once in ossining they get their three squares and maybe find the gumption to pull themselves up get educated in the library there after attica ossining's got the best from what i hear state prison library i mean

in all 16 demonstrators were detained it is thought that four others managed to get away lieutenant ww expressed confidence that those four perpetrators would be apprehended within 48 hours the only information the arrested black demonstrators would give police is they live in the hunts point section of the bronx and their surnames are dead each of the 16 said the same thing his name was curtis dead willie dead lincoln dead floyd dead like that dead

---

*Butterfly McQueen—a Hollywood prototype of the black female servant. Most popularly known as Prissy in *Gone With the Wind*.

THREE

BOY GEORGE

Couldn't sleep / we got in the car / VCR / we went to the F
Street store / adult matter / open all night / rear-door entry / we
rented a video / five gals-three studs / fascists are sexier / I did
some quick math / three orifices unengaged / two airports
attacked by terrorists / on to the TV monitor / on to the
waterbed / we snorted a line / we watched the tape / we did our
shit / we phone-ordered Sushi / was it good for you / of the
eight seven were blond / one was Oriental / the Oriental was
blond / international terrorism / tattoo all AIDS carriers / one
was transsexual / did you order through a catalog / we started
with foreplay / blame it on Libya / sweet snatch / big dick / no
European airport is safe / how big is big / coordinated at-
tacks / the boy delivering our Sushi looked like Boy George /
who's he / the loop kept spinning / the Oriental was transsexual / blood and bodies everywhere / pull back the sheath / use
both hands / close-up for a cum shot / he-she had the goods /
use both hands and your tongue / what is terrorism / certain
orifices still unengaged / then what / then we plunged into the
Sushi / how many times did you get off / the Sushi was pretty /
Boy George was calculating / the networks are calculating /
want a chunk of the action / Mau-Mau Shiites / forty-six
percent of all American homes have them / here comes a cum
shot / the new old patriotism / I'm talking about video / TV
viewing patterns will never be the same / network bigs corner-
ing congressmen / bloody reprisals likely / no big deal says the
government / who are the real terrorists / we he'ped tobacca
we'll he'p you all / we were still horny / you like pro football /

the loop kept spinning / we did another line / wall to wall action / daisy chain / we ordered more Sushi / what about those orifices / where are the sex toys / Kalashnikov rifles / the mafia own pornography / everybody loves a winner / Boy George was a winner / for half an hour / remember Johnny Stompanato / what is the institutionalized avant-garde / peel my banana / who owns the mafia / Ethiopian food aid / get on your knees / what if you have AIDS / who wants to be Jewish / oh do it harder / we enlisted the delivery boy / the shadowy splinter group of the PLO / it's *not* a health hazard / after relieving him of his Sushi / how many times did you get off / Boy George is making a comeback / dangerous sex can kill you / he has reconstituted his image / the loop kept spinning / how is it spread / thank God for the Mafia / via TV / they own pornography / that's what we're told / they own heroin / Johnny Stompanato phoned Lana Turner / said what I got you never seen before / she wasn't so bad herself / discovered sipping an ice cream soda / nothing's off limits / stay away from asbestos / in her sweater at the counter of Schwab's / in spite of Manville Corporation's assurances / on Sunset Boulevard / Boy George knows how to move it / AIDS began in darkest Africa / we ordered more Sushi / we pressed fast-forward / we heard the doorbell ring / how dark is darkest / a delivery girl with our Sushi / if skyjacking scares you don't fly / she was blond and beautiful / geez look at them bazookas / why should the world get sucked into the Arab-Jewish thing / Boy George wants another half hour / let them kill their own damn selves / he'll have to consult Tiresias Warhol / what comes after nausea / great weather for football / if you do fly do some homework / she slipped out of her jeans / much recent literature on how to communicate with terrorists / the delivery girl was Boy George / that deft disguiser / in case you're kidnaped or sky-jacked / three studs / five gals / one transsexual / there's a chapter on how to relate to your ear being cut off / Muslims brutally infibulate their women / wall to wall action / all nature abhors a vacuum / time is money / plug them holes up Johnny / is Buddha-nature nature / we decorated our bodies with Sushi /Americans are darn tired of ingratitude / the transsexual was resourceful / the heck with the chopsticks / hi-tech reconstructive surgery / which of our U.S. presidents was a transsexual / can implant another ear in no time / don't say Teddy Roosevelt / it's tougher than ever being truthful / if you can *afford* the surgery / right . . . there / oh that feels good / you say you want high technology / wouldn't you risk losing an ear to tour the Holy Land / in five years you will be able to get born / live / die / without ever leaving your modular unit / here comes a cum shot / we turned off the VCR / how many times did you get off / we still couldn't sleep / too much damn Sushi / got up and ran a bath / used our just-bought bath oil / called Deep Creep / bought in the F Street store / smells like anise / flipped on the TV / designed to promote erotic weariness / Headline News reports another terrorist attack / all natural ingredients / made in California / home of irradiated testicles / no problem they were only prisoners / besides it will benefit our space program / Boy George is a vegetarian / Strategic Defense Initiative / also known as Star Wars / the producers have threatened suit / it was *their* doggone movie / slip a daisy in your Uzi / snap a photo / sell the photo / make a bundle / joint attack on Paris' Orly Airport / and a synagogue in Brussels / turned off the TV / flipped on the VCR / Soviet-designed automatic weapons / hand grenades / slipped in another tape / X-rated naturally / Coca-Cola cocksman / considerable carnage / Coke big doubles as male stud narc dick / maybe it's the other way around / too much hokey narrative / fast-forward / who's number one / define ideology / blond coke stud exec / gray at the temples / flies first class to Hawaii / since they are pathologically insecure make a point of not alienating your skyjackers / complicitous stewardess / well-developed labia / selectively called hottentot apron / Honolulu at last / Winnie Mandela arrested a third time / in two weeks / surf / scurf / high-rise / sea-front / sexecutive suites / according to Headline News / that "radical black activist" / we had a smoke / top-grade Hawaiian / twenty-three years in prison / fun-drugs can kill you / I'm talking about Nelson Mandela / China Lee and Jade Fong / polysexual poon pancakes / black freedom-mongering his crime / six holes not nearly enough /

for our Coke biggie / they ripped out his prostate / super rich
hung blond executive / we adjusted our VCR / all manner of
orifices / crush the terrorist ANC / sunbathing gals / species
Southern California / additional big dicks / thirty-four killed /
nearly two hundred injured / two languid male surfers / I'm
talking about Orly and Brussels / Palestinian terrorists / so
we've got five gals / three machos / Soviet-designed automatic
weapons / make that three and a half / Coca Cola big's got
more / I think I'm horny all over again / God's made a comeback on the campus / what comes after nausea / he can take
some off there / add some on there / I'm not talking hippy
Hinduism / cult stuff / he's a cosmetic miracle-maker / what
can I stick in my mouth / surgery in Orange County / ROTC
also / How many times did you get off / work hard / work hard
at playing hard / within sight of Disneyland / you can never be
too hung / you've got to be positive / so is AIDS / winning is
contagious / so is AIDS / gal-gal / stud-gal / stud-gals / stud-
stud never / three-forty a.m. / I still can't sleep / state-of-the-art
sex toys / take the U.K. / now even they want to be winners /
have *you* been tested / wall to wall action / not with this current
strain of terrorism / AIDS came via darkest Africa / stick it to
the coal miners / generated out of Idi Amin's gargantuan thigh /
what about those unfilled holes / stick it to the IRA / Boy
George is British / the question was "what makes *you* cream" /
stick it to the black majority / Muslims brutally mutilate trespassers / so much for Honolulu hugger-mugger / an estimated
70 percent of gays are carrying the virus / committed as they
are to world domination / time out while Coke big concludes a
deal in a sea-front high-rise / fast-forward / how many times did
you get off / four-eighteen a.m. / the city never sleeps / anyway
time is body time / create your own space / sixty by sixty lot /
my prostate's about had it for tonight / the single most seminal
porn flick / facing the freeway / of all time / I'd say Deep Throat
with Linda Lovelace / certain matchups should be strenuously
avoided / Libya-Israel for example / comparable in its way to
Citizen Kane / yet Lovelace didn't make diddly / I won't sleep
tonight but you will / while I watch King's Row on video / the
great communicator's all-time favorite / in which he plays a

déclassé young stud / courting a surgeon's daughter / gets into a train accident / after which the class-proud surgeon / maliciously amputates both of the young suitor's legs / this is the flick that made the young stud a star / remember his celebrated line / "Where is the rest of me" / became the title of his runaway / smash / best-selling autobiography / you're not talking about Boy George again / are you / no / I'm not /

VIDEO / VIDEO

This is Bourgeois' story.

Those who survived lived in superstructures. Four multi-storied structures erected atop the broad base of devastated government buildings in what was formerly called the Capitol. Each structure was erected so that it looked out on a parterre which opened to the east. Though plantings had not yet grown in the parterre, the "artifice-flora" implanted as an "interim measure" was colorful and, from a distance, flourishing.

You ask me to date the Devastation. It happened not long after the great advertising agencies went global. As one of the VP's of one of the competing ad agencies put it back then: "We now have the ballast and technology to deliver to the major global corporations of the free world an unmatched depth of client service, creative talent and media-buying muscle."

Each superstructure had its governing body which was appointed by the plenary body of the entire settlement. The organizational model of governance was the "Auschwitz Detention Center for Undesirables" instituted by the Germans during the Second Great War in Soviet Poland.

Because of the still-great danger of contamination on the blighted avenues, each inhabitant (or in exceptional circumstances inhabitants) remained in his/her unit, was strictly denied access to the outside, and had no direct intercourse with neighbors. Inhabitants were permitted to transmit messages to the Body. Food and basic medical supplies were requisitioned electronically and delivered in radiation-resistant containers. Bi-monthly "councils" were conducted via the inhabitants' TV receivers. There was no provision for surgery or medical crisis. The Body had concluded that the ever-present risk of contamination precluded unmediated intercourse under any circumstances.

I said that the governance model was Auschwitz. Except for the gassing. Instead of gas were TV receivers, one to every unit. Bourgeois? He was among those termed "Kapo": one of two charged to "nourish" each superstructure, in his instance structure 2. To this end, Bourgeois, in radiation-resistant coveralls and toting a sack of light-weight video cassettes, was fitted into a harness and suspended outside his structure. By means of an electronically powered system he was deposited in front of individual unit-windows.

Inlaid into the stone façade to the left of each window was a standardized video cassette recorder (VCR), which, when engaged, displayed on the receiver within the unit. It was left to the Kapo to select the video cassette in accord with the dreams and remnant desires of the particular inhabitant.

It should be stated that since the windows were both sound- and shatter-proof, only mimed communication passed between Kapo and inhabitant. The Kapo's responsibility included not only recollecting a given inhabitant's best-loved videos, but selecting a video which would (as the Charter put it) "buttress the inhabitant's self-concept."

Here Bourgeois is now suspended in front of the 29th floor window of unit M. Pressed as close to the window away from the active wind as he dares. The pale, gaunt, middle-aged man within is naked, gesturing spasmodically, Bourgeois attending to the gestures. It is a violent passion the inhabitant recaps, though he himself is obviously far from aroused. He strokes and tugs at his loose breasts, makes lustful penetrating stabs with his fists, rolls his eyes, spits furiously . . . It is not one of his lengthier pantomimes. As Bourgeois responds with certain abbreviated gestures (called "semaphores"), 29 M vehemently nods his head. Bourgeois extracts a tape of *Miami Vice,* March 1986, from his sack and inserts it into the VCR. At once inhabitant 29 M, mouth open, scurries closer to his receiver. When Crockett (Don Johnson), pretty commodity-stud, moves (cool-vice-slick-dick-moves), 29 M in his cramped unit moves with him. And when Crockett talks (hard-guy-big-heart-mono-tone-pieties), 29 M talks with him, talks *as* him.

The institutionalized talk of the late 80s, which preceded the Devastation, was uninflected, a passion-pastiche, a sweet ice, a glittery shell. The institutionalized talk was the obverse of the institutionalized thought, sometimes called Postmodernism, and described by one of its Praetorian Guard as "a new gratification in surfaces and accompanied by a whole new ground tone in which the pathos of high modernism has been inverted . . ."

Bourgeois signals into his transmitter, moves on. As indicated, the Kapo's nourishment rounds were electronically generated, but he was dependent on technicians to portage him from story to story and window to window according to his transmitted directions. And because "Kapoing" occupied his entire day and was exhausting, he depended on technicians to inspect and maintain his harness and pulleys.

Bourgeois' contact with his technicians was incorporeal. Physical contact existed only between the inhabitants of a specific unit, and because of the fear of contamination fewer and fewer units contained more than a single individual. Even long-married couples were commonly persuaded to dwell apart and to communicate via the system. The fact was that even now, nearly eight years after the Devastation, the Pestilence was capable of fulminating suddenly in an apparently healthy constitution. Consequently, it was usual even for children to dwell alone; of course the psychic strain was considerable. Which was where the Kapo came in.

Bourgeois is suspended in front of the window of unit 32 F, belonging to a thirteen-year-old girl separated from her mother, who resides on a lower floor (her father and two siblings killed in the initial aftermath). As usual she lies on her side, frail knees-to-head, wrapped in a coarse woolen blanket. Seeing Bourgeois at her window, she pricks up her ears like a burrowing animal about to be fed. The Kapo, smiling through his mask, semaphores broadly. The young girl's eyes shine. Bourgeois reaches into his sack and withdraws *MADONNA DOES CARNEGIE,* which he inserts into the VCR. Meanwhile the girl in her soiled cotton nightie is on her feet, twisting her pale, thin torso, her blotched child's arms raised to her hair, orgasmically stroking her hair with Madonna, pouting with Madonna, mouthing as Madonna's mouths the 1986 mega-hit, "Like a Virgin," *which as much as any other single factor was instrumental in switching young Americans back to the traditional values of home and family, which in the 80s amounted to a kind of "inverted pathos," also called survivalism, since the social revolution of the 60s had become the millenarianism of the 80s, and just about everyone lower-middle class or better was into "rapture," either via Real Estate or Pentecostalism.*

Through his mask through the window Bourgeois watches the girl squirm and kick and sing. He then signals into his transmitter. No response. A second time he instructs the technician, NZ, to portage him to a unit two stories below. Still no response. NZ is drunk, as he always is on what used to be called "Saturday," one of the residuals from before the Devastation. Having previously (fruitlessly) appealed to the Body to remove NZ, Bourgeois accumulates yet further proof that Kapoing, which meant so much in the months following the Devastation, now counts for little.

Finally, drunken NZ responds, portages Bourgeois down to 30 J. This is one of the most turbulent areas on superstructure 2, and Bourgeois has to tighten his hood and compress his body in order to reduce somewhat the fierce impact of the wind. Within, the elderly black couple—one of the small number who refused to separate—are praying. When Bourgeois had begun six years ago, he assumed that the couple were pantomiming prayer to convey to him a best-loved video. He subsequently learned that they were literally praying.

Most of the records were destroyed in the Devastation or during the Pestilence, so Bourgeois had no specific data on this couple. They were among a very small percentage of non-whites who survived. Both looked to be in their seventies. Each wore the same resolutely devout expression. And they prayed.

Their best-loved video was church service, but since there were no black church services in the Kapo's bag of tricks, they usually settled for the telegenic white multimillionaire populist preacher from Louisiana, Jimmy Swaggart, or for the late 80s black family comedy, *The Cosby Show,* which is what they wanted today. Bourgeois, smiling, gave it to them, waved, signaled into his transmitter, waited for NZ, moved on.

I said this was Bourgeois' story. In truth the other Kapos are named Bourgeois as well, though as a concession to narrative expectations I have called them Exxon, Terrorist, Sex Therapy, Baseball, Prayer-in-the-Schools, Indian Genocide, and Gene Splicing. Look now: Bourgeois semaphoring to an inhabitant on the 33rd floor; Terrorist, the lone female Kapo, nourishing an inhabitant in the same structure nine floors down. On structure 3, there is Gene Splicing being portaged up to the 37th story, the insistent wind rippling his rad-resistant coveralls; on structure 4, Prayer-in-the-Schools portaged laterally on the 19th floor . . .

In the aftermath of the Devastation there had been a broad tolerance for what was called "Omega Humanism." The Devastation had stripped the survivors of their rigidities, inducing a fellow-feeling which resembled love. It was at this juncture that the interlocking notions of the Kapo and the best-loved videos were conceived as the best methods of humanizing a situation where contamination made actual contact untenable.

But as months became years, and as the Pestilence showed signs of lingering beyond the life span of even the youngest survivors, fellow-feeling gave way to fatalism, anomie. It even gave way in some quarters to cruelty and sadism, and the sole reason these were not more widespread was the dearth of bodily contact.

The first Charter after the Devastation had assigned each able-bodied (and mentally unfractured) adult survivor a specific employment. Most of these assignments were basically morale-boosters, since with the prohibition of bodily contact opportunities for real employment were severely limited. The technicians upon whom the Kapos depended were exceptions—their employment *was* critical. Unfortunately, in line with the recent gloomy conviction that the Pestilence would outlast the survivors, the current technicians were generally among those who cared only for their *own* nourishment and inclined not to extend themselves beyond a nominal adherence to the tenets of their employment. Thus in the last year-and-a-half two Kapos—Exxon and Gene Splicing—fell to their deaths in "accidents" which might have been prevented had the technicians been sensitive, or even alert.

The Kapos tried in their way to counter the lassitude and cynicism. Clearly, the ideal response would have been to engage the people, the great majority of inhabitants not part of the governing body. But the compelled reliance on a single communications system which was in the employ of the Body made contact with the people problematic. When (via semaphores) the Kapos "discussed" the possibility of erecting a competing system, the Body got word and threatened to withdraw all material support from Kapoing.

For the time being, then, the Kapos concluded that the best course was to seek out a way of successfully rupturing the system, while continuing with their nourishment rounds. Soon after this decision was made, Terrorist, the lower-story Kapo for superstructure 2, plunged to her death from the 18th floor. Accident? The Body's version of moral suasion? Bourgeois could not be certain.

Bourgeois was now singly responsible for nourishing the entire superstructure. This was more than physically formidable, since he would have to become acquainted with the dreams, remnant desires—and best-loved videos—of scores of inhabitants he had never nourished. When Bourgeois asked the Body for a replacement for Terrorist, he was instructed to make a formal appeal. Nothing happened. After several further appeals the Body informed him that because of the physical risk, radiation danger, and flat-out hard work, no one was willing to replace Terrorist; nor was the Body in a position to assign someone this employment against his/her will.

One of Terrorist's former units on the 17th floor contained a couple in their mid- to late-twenties and an infant. For obvious reasons, the most proximate of which was that a mother would have to deliver her own child, there were virtually no new births. Evidently couple 17 H had decided to take the considerable risk; their girl-child must have been a few months old, and she was nurtured entirely within their unit.

To Bourgeois, suspended outside their window-cell, the young parents mimed their passion for space, trees, underbrush, flowing water, broad sky; the father holding his infant with one arm, gesturing with the other. Bourgeois reflected, then withdrew a NBC nature video called "The Intelligence of Elephants," filmed in the great "First-World" zoos, as well as on location in east-central Africa *(this was filmed in 1991; the*

"Horn" of Africa was radiated the following year). Bourgeois engaged the cassette and through the window saw it display on the TV receiver. The couple, though, did not even acknowledge it; they remained in front of the window, pitifully miming.

It was not until five weeks later that Bourgeois was portaged in front of their window a second time. No one was within. Bourgeois was subsequently informed of the following: 17 H, couple and infant, defying official strictures, exited their unit, appropriated one of the two small elevators, and went outside. After walking for some time they located a tree that was still alive, and assuming this was a safe place they sat and then slept. Only the mother awakened, and she briefly, dying that same evening of the Pestilence. This was the Body's version, conveyed to them, they said, by one of their "surveillance helicopters."

That the Pestilence was still active was, for Bourgeois, too often evidenced. Every third nourishment round, it seemed, uncovered another death, and sometimes more. Elderly men seemed especially vulnerable, and the peculiar symptoms could not easily be confused with other species of death.

Because Bourgeois now had twice the number of units to nourish and so didn't see particular inhabitants for five or six weeks at a time, several of his regulars withdrew beyond succoring. Having depended on Bourgeois' bi-weekly visits, they soon became convinced that he had either abandoned them or died. Of course Bourgeois had anticipated this response after Terrorist's death, and he had specifically requested the Body to notify the inhabitants that their Kapo would be unavoidably delayed; it was never done.

NZ, in his cups, has portaged Bourgeois to 19 M. The woman within must have been a serious actress before the Devastation. She had been Terrorist's charge; Bourgeois nourished her just three times before, and each time she refused to request a best-loved video. Instead she made up her face radically and expertly mimed what appeared to be three sequential roles: first the innocent child-faced clown; then the egocentric, competitive young man; third, the scripture-quoting, middle-aged war-technocrat.

Bourgeois' visits occurred every five-and-a-half or six weeks. And the fourth time he was deposited in front of her window she was as usual prepared for him. It took the Kapo some time to decipher what she was about—but then he saw. Naked and bent over her cot, she had made up her outthrust buttocks and vulva to represent a scene of violence: *a tiny female and male in tandem ponderously balancing on their shoulders an archaic, cumbersome musket or cannon, aimed at a creature that is at once both monster and superstructure. The creature is bleeding from its "head," and in the coursing blood are the anguished disembodied faces and mangled body parts of inhabitants.* This was how Bourgeois saw it.

Her "tableau" displayed, she then stood and turned to Bourgeois her face. She had blackened her face so that not even the ridge of her nose was apparent, and on this plane she had meticulously painted in gold-green a single tall wavering grass or bullrush.

That was it. Bourgeois witnessed, without semaphore, without reference to his sack of best-loved videos. He waved a nervous goodbye, signalled into the transmitter, moved on.

Despite increasing fatigue, Bourgeois had no choice but to Kapo longer hours. The problem here was that his technicians refused to increase *their* hours, and Bourgeois had to appeal to the Body. Surprisingly, the Body acted upon his request, but instead of increasing work-time for the existing technicians, they added another technician to superstructure 2. The new man, KKX, was like NZ a heavy drinker, was unacquainted with the system, and evidently resented having to learn it.

A constellation of unfortunate events occurred in the week

after KKX was employed as a technician. First, Prayer-in-the-Schools, the single remaining Kapo for superstructure 3, fell to his death from an upper floor. Then the Pestilence took hold of three middle stories in superstructure 1, and the units in that area were quarantined. Within ten days only four of the forty-three inhabitants had not died. Lastly, the inhabitants in each of the superstructures were denied free access to their transmitters.

Until now an inhabitant had been entitled to transmit messages to the Body during waking hours, and an emergency message at any time. In accord with an ordinance in the Charter, all of these messages were logged and at least a portion of them were acknowledged. But now the body decreed that the inhabitants would be permitted to transmit for just one half-hour in the morning and another half-hour in the late afternoon. Inhabitants attempting to transmit outside these times were subject to punishment. This new decree seemed capricious, and its effect was scarcely compatible with "buttressing the inhabitants' self-concept." The five remaining Kapos appealed it, but to no effect.

The inhabitants' initial response to the Body's latest stricture was, so far as Bourgeois could determine, a kind of numbness. But within a few weeks this had changed dramatically. First certain individuals left their units and clustered in other units with their families or former friends. They talked and laughed nervously, and some couples related sexually. Bourgeois, from his privileged access, was surprised that these encounters were not more desperate and delirious than they appeared.

The Body permitted the physical contact to continue for two full days; then, via the unit receivers *and* the receivers in each superstructure employed for "contingencies," the Body restated its interdiction on direct contact. However, at this stage interdiction meant little, and several of the groups even left their superstructure for the outside. More amazing than this initiative was the fact that none—not a single individual—contracted the Pestilence.

That incredible knowledge spread rapidly through the settlement and within a few days there were clusters of survivors outside every superstructure. Children, parents, even the elderly, were leaving or preparing to leave their units, and there was not a single case of the Pestilence among them.

Then it happened. The Body announced in premonitory tones that nine of the absconding inhabitants had contracted the Pestilence, that those who left their units would not be permitted back, and that henceforth departures would be subject to "termination with extreme prejudice" (this last, borrowed from the U.S. engagement against the Vietnamese communists in the 60s and 70s, was justified under the "Emergency Provisions," one of several codicils to the first Charter). At the time of this annunciation there must have been thirty-five or forty inhabitants on the outside.

After having exchanged veiled semaphores with the other Kapos, Bourgeois was actually in one of the small elevators of superstructure 2, on his way outside, when the Body intervened with still another announcement: nine more of the "absconders" had become contaminated, and the Body had been compelled to "void" the entire number to forestall widespread infection.

Bourgeois hesitated. He felt certain—or almost certain—that the Body lied about the contamination. The outside, Bourgeois believed, was no longer infected. Yet for him to leave now was to leave alone. Clearly the best course would be for each Kapo to convey to his people the necessity to leave, not individually, but cohesively, en masse.

KKX has portaged Bourgeois to the 19th floor. The actress, her face painted blood-red, has somehow trussed herself to the cot. No, she is simulating. She is on her back on her cot in a rough white shift, her arms and legs spread-eagled. Bourgeois is trying to semaphore to her the urgency of leaving her unit, banding with the others, *seizing control.* She is too engrossed in her drama. Bourgeois cannot make himself understood.

Bourgeois tries again in front of another unit-window, but the couple within want video: Belushi, Ackroyd, Gilda Radner—the madcap gang from the original *Saturday Night Live.* The woman has already distended her face into the Gilda Radner-plastic-mouth-clown-face and is displaying her long Gilda Radner-legs. Bourgeois, reaching into his video sack, gives them their *Saturday Night Live.*

In front of a third window Bourgeois attempts to convey his urgent message. But here too the middle-aged man will not understand, and when Bourgeois delays in giving him his *60 Minutes* (the celebrated CBS "news magazine" show of the 70s and 80s), the man collapses and weeps, weeps uncontrollably.

Soon enough—and unexpectedly—the Body abandoned its papal-pronunciamiento tone, relaxed its strictures and returned unlimited transmission to the inhabitants. Meanwhile four more inhabitants died of the Pestilence in superstructure 3. And another Kapo, Indian Genocide, of superstructure 4, fell to his death. That left one Kapo for 1, 2, and 4, and none at all for superstructure 3.

Bourgeois himself? Continued his rounds. Video nourishment. He believed in his work, thought it amounted to doing one's best under appalling circumstances. About the Body, his feelings were conflicted, but wasn't the Body, finally, an encumbrance to be lived with? Bourgeois thought so. Bourgeois died in situ, *fell to his death. The Body replaced Bourgeois with another Kapo, male, whose name is also Bourgeois, but whom I will call Culture-of-Silence.*

RAY (SPIKE) MILLAND

—So, how was London?

—We saw a lot of vampire movies.

—How come?

—They were playing around, at the arty film houses.

(Pause)

—How was the weather?

—Do you remember the dark and light in Fritz Lang's *Ministry of Fear,* 1943? With Ray Milland? Did you know that Ray Milland acted under the name Spike Milland? At the start of his career?

—Ray Milland as Spike? I can't see it.

—You know those drawings Henry Moore did of Londoners huddling in the subways during the Blitz?

—Sorry, I don't.

—Pity.

(Pause)

—You rode the tube?

—All the time.

—What about the Punks?

—Still happening. Tattoos on their arms reading "Auschwitz Was A Gas."

—That's their politics?

—Right. A plague on all your houses.

—Drugs?

—Cheap booze, heroin. The working-class poisons. They have—the Punks—a post-Holocaust glaze about them. After such knowledge what forgiveness?

—Sounds familiar. Auden?

—Eliot.

(Pause)

—Why did you mention Moore's drawings of the Blitz?

—His light. And Lang's in *Ministry of Fear*. I saw that same dark and light in London.

—What would the Punks do during a Blitz?

—They seem, you know, many of them, less British than . . . pandemic. A kind of spastic, spiky futility, produced in Thatcher's U.K., but bottled in the U.S. Distributed by the Japanese.

—Japanese Punks?

—Japanese yuppies. I saw them wherever I went, in Yorkshire, in Scotland.

—The yen.

—You know the circa-World-War-II stereotype: Japan bowed low, in silent deep disdain? They've stopped bowing.

—That's a break.

—Japanese families of four—nuclear families—travelling in northern Scotland. Young Japanese women travelling in pairs, solo.

—Really?

—A bit hard about the eyes. Very un-geisha. Changing yen for pounds.

(Pause)

—How does it go for Labour?

—Silent on Ireland. Courting the Blacks.

—*Are* they?

—Lip sync. Neck but don't pet. They're very coy.

—Labour?

—Yes.

—They want to get elected.

—Yes. They're eminently sensible on nuclear proliferation.

—They'd just as soon not die.

(Pause)

—The other evening we went to the National Film Theatre to see *Love on the Dole*, 1941. Working-class Manchester during the Depression. With Deborah Kerr as the clear-sighted, realpolitik-daughter who chooses prostitution for her hungry family's sake. The writer—Walter Greenwood—tried to get the film out in the Thirties when it might matter, but the British censors thought it too inflammatory. When we left the theatre—this was Sunday about eleven p.m.—we must have walked past fifty or sixty vagrants and heroin addicts slumped against the dark sides of the building near Waterloo Bridge. It was raining. In the flickering light from the Thames and from the inside of the theatre I could see them slumped against the building. I wish Henry Moore or someone would draw *them*. Title it "Forty-five Years After The Blitz." (Pause) In Fritz Lang's version of the Blitz Ray Milland spends the night in the subway with his arm around Marjorie Reynolds and his hair unmussed.

—Ray Milland's hair?

—Yes, and his nose. He had a lovely nose.

—A Ray Milland not a Spike Milland nose?

—In *Ministry of Fear* Marjorie Reynolds plays a beautiful and virtuous German refugee who as a result of falling in love with Ray Milland murders her Nazi brother. Do you know what happened to her?

—Tell me.

—She ended up on TV as resilient Peg, wife to William Bendix on *The Life of Riley*.

(Pause)

—I saw Milland on TV recently. Shortly before he died. He was bald and drawn, pathetically nostalgic.

—Pity.

—He had to be close to eighty.

—A long life on the celluloid.

(Pause)

—I said "in Fritz Lang's version of the Blitz," but Lang had to kick against the pricks at every stage. When after twenty years he finally left Hollywood he did it, he said, to salvage his mental health. What I'm saying is that the several hokey un-Graham Greene touches in *Ministry of Fear* had to have been imposed by the studio.

(Long pause)

—What was I saying?

—Fritz Lang.

—What about him?

—Lang and the dark and light of *Ministry of Fear,* how it resembles the Henry Moore drawings of the Londoners in the subway during the Blitz, both of which resemble, with signal differences, London 1985.

—The year of South Africa / AIDS-phobia / *Rambo*-mania / *Dallas* Does England.

—Yes. What are you up to now?

—Not much.

—Not drinking too much?

—Noo.

(Pause)

—Are the Punks afraid?

—They're afraid to stand still.

—There *ought* to be a Ministry of Fear.

—Yes. An Exchequer of Fear. World-wide like the World Bank. Dispensing loans to Third and Fourth and Fifth World countries who demonstrate the prerequisite fear. Afterwards dunning them mercilessly. Imposing liens on their rice paddies. On their genitals.

(Pause)

—How was the beer? In London?

—Gone downhill. Served up ice cold as in America. Budweiser Lite with all its additives in most of the pubs. Difficult to write while sipping Bud Lite, ice-cold.

—Yes, your passport describes you as a writer. But that is a very elastic term.

—Hang on. (Pause) Greenstreet to Lorre in *The Mask of Dimitrios,* 1946. After the Eric Ambler spy chiller.

—1944. Otherwise excellent.

—There is, you know, a movement to bring back real British bitter. Yorkshire in the forefront here. Many of the same folks who want real British bitter in, want the Punks and Pakis and Africans out. (Pause) Henry Moore is from Yorkshire. Is he still alive?

—I believe he is. Is Francis Bacon still alive?

—Yes. In fact I saw a new Bacon show at the Tate. Seems that Bacon has recently tried to move away from his well-documented, almost commodified, and now—with AIDS—rather problematic, sodomy-cum-crucifixion.

—Move away where?

—Uncertain. Three or four of his latest things have a kind of deliberately blurred outline, color looking for purchase.

—Isn't sodomy more than ever a kind of crucifixion? With the AIDS propaganda and the rest of it?

—It is. The question is how to package it. Existential despair has lost *its* purchase.

—Though the majority of people are in worse shape?

—Yes.

(Pause)

—But you saw vampire movies?

—Yes. And in Highgate Cemetery where Karl Marx and George Eliot and Galsworthy and Colonel Blimp and Bram Stoker are buried, the guide said that a tomb was violated six or seven months ago—the vandals planted stakes through the coffins and chests of the cadavers.

—For a lark?

—The cadavers were Jews.

—I see.

—As Jews they were buried in unconsecrated ground. But in an imposing tomb, since they had been wealthy and presumably wanted to dramatize it.

—Unconsecrated ground?

—Yes.

(Pause)

—There's a lot of anti-Israel sentiment these days. You think it's connected to that?

—I wouldn't expect anti-Israelis to respond in just that way, no.

—Punks?

—Punks are promoted to like sex. And racial "purity" slash fascism is, we're informed, sexier than socialism. But calculated cemetery vampirism? I'd say no.

—Punks are also promoted to be daft. Paranoid schizophrenia *generates* racial "purity" slash fascism—and is also sexier than socialism, isn't it?

—Is it?

—What do you have up your sleeve?

—A thin long arm.

(Pause)

—What if Ray Milland had stayed with Spike Milland?

—Spike Milland. I like the ring of it. My guess is it would have changed the course of the last fifty years.

—In which direction?

—In the right direction, the honest-gambler direction, the John Huston direction. Huston, interviewed in a recent *Playboy,* said he liked Gable and Mitchum and Bogart but didn't much care for Montgomery Clift whose eyes, according to Huston, tended to well with tears. Huston, by the way, is dying tough, of emphysema, on a remote backwater in Mexico. He's bedded broads, kicked ass, directed movies on several continents, and he is altogether pleased with himself. For a time he was an advocate of vaguely populist causes but managed not to be grilled by HUAC. He is unsympathetic toward those who were grilled, whose careers and lives were destroyed thereby, because, as he says, many of them in fact *were* communists.

(Pause)

—This is the Highland Chieftain from Inverness to King's Cross Station, London, calling at Pitlochry, Perth, Gleneagles, Dunblane, Stirling, Larbert, Falkirk Grahamston, Miles, Haymarket, Edinburgh, Newcastle, Darlington, York, and London.

—What's that about?

—Infrastructure. I'm wondering how far England can bend without either snapping or being twisted utterly out of shape.

—Ah.

—Come to think of it, in twenty years there likely won't be a "first world" country that isn't psychically air-brushed, lip sync'd, homogenized.

(Pause)

—Do you believe that?

—What?

—Homogenization in twenty years?

—Unless there's a decisive intervention: people's revolution, nuclear holocaust, a capsule that promotes unlegislated dreaming.

(Pause)

—Poor England.

—Not at all. The U.K. won't allow itself to feel sorry for itself. And my ardent wish is that they achieve a fate consistent with this virtue.

—You're mocking.

—Yes.

—And exaggerating. You're an alarmist. A kind of reasoning millenarian. Except the reasoning is specious, twisted into conformity with something in yourself that is marginal, even dangerous.

—Dangerous to whom?

—To yourself. Likely to the empire. And you know what else?

—Say it.

—Your wife is a filthy cook.

—Very good. Ray Spike Milland.

—Tell me from where.

—*Dial M For Murder.* 1954. Hitchcock.

U.K., 7.85
U.S., 2.86, 6.87

LIGHTNIN' HOPKINS

"Got the bourgeois blues, gonna spread the news all around"
Leadbelly

Inside, the black-felon is waiting on the governor: the black-felon will be executed with a lethal injection, or he will be granted clemency and re-sentenced to life imprisonment without parole.

First was the American Legion-type old guy, said he played kids' hardball with Ted Williams, and, yeah, Williams hit the ball great then too. Then the middle-aged Italian with the hard-guy scowl and the limp. Finally the thirtyish yuppie manager with the reptilian face and glasses. They had Bourgeois up against the wall in the corner of the lot, the yuppie pressing his case for paying his price, Bourgeois playing the oppressed consumer while watching himself play the oppressed consumer. Bottom line: they trussed Bourgeois up on the "long bed" of the brand new G.M.C. pickup and hoisted him from the neon marquee. Just joking. Bourgeois bought their G.M.C. pickup.

Bourgeois in a brand new G.M.C. pickup.
Progressive Bourgeois in a brand new G.M.C. pickup.
Progressive Bourgeois with his attaché case and umbrella in a brand new G.M.C. pickup. *Repeat this mantra and the umbrella turns into an M-16 assault rifle.*
Lightnin' Hopkins in a brand new G.M.C. pickup, guitar in the gun-rack.
Lightnin' ain't *in* the truck, he's out the truck, footin' it on the "75 highway" outside Dallas, "black man trying to flag a

ride."*

"Walkin' the jivin' highway, heat and fumes. Tell you what: it's better'n pickin' cotton. Better'n pullin' corn."

"Jus' watch out they don't stick your black ass in jail."

"Man, whatchoo talkin' 'bout? This is 1986."

"Thas what I'm talkin' 'bout."

1984 plus 2: Capital has recycled the saddle-shoes-Fifties *along with* the Victorian version of schizophrenia: fated-loony brain not maladjusted human, not political prisoner, not polluted context, plaster fated-loony brain with pharmaceuticals, not the generic kind not as good as the name brands, zonk the sucker while protecting your property from drug-crazed intruders, while investing in pharmaceutical-parent-corporations, while shoeing your pink precious daughter in spiffy white and red saddle-shoes. Lightnin' sings: "Les you and me stop off at this yere bar and get our heads tore up."*

Bourgeois' head aches. He's lost his appetite.

Sounds like terminal nausea.

"I growed up with the blues."*

Bourgeois don't know where to turn.

He turns again to the twisting form in the too-sweet night, strange fruit, magnolia aerosol bomb, classic formula.

Cut my brother down.

Bourgeois has lost his appetite but not his fire. Not his fire. Please underscore that.

Bourgeois is liable to set himself ablaze.

Like the Vietnamese Buddhists during the Vietnam War.

Then what?

Brer-rabbit-Lightnin'. Tip your hat but don't take off the shades. Made your first guitar out of a cigar box. Centerville Texas. Seven-years-old you heard Blind Lemon Jefferson playing in the street, played with him. Blind Lemon said: "Who's that?" Someone said, "It's just a little kid messin' around." Blind Lemon said, "he ain't messin', he *playin'*."* The Hopkins family all played guitar, except for Mother Hopkins

who played some accordion, church music and such. Lightnin'
made his way by bus or by flagging rides and when black folks
heard how he could play that thing "they'd take me in, warm
me, feed me, fix me a paper sack of food"*: THE SOUTH AS
HANGMAN BLUES.

"They turn 'round I'm gone. Which is one reason they called
me Lightnin'."

"What are some other reasons?"

(Laughs) "I'd ruther sing these other reasons than talk
'em." Lightnin' picks a few funky chords on the guitar. "No
money, babe, / I jus' got a old wrist-watch on my arm."*

Art to tell time by.

Art as mirror / lamp / Molotov cocktail.

Art as resistance.

Decode it then resist it.

Decode what?

Ideology, Decentered Center, Cynical Synod, Late-Corpo-
rate Capital.

Bourgeois just wants to blues.

He's the chief of grief when the call come he got to go.

Bourgeois heard Lightnin' tell a ramblin' story about a white
pig. White pig equals local constabulary. White pig equals
national constabulary. White pig equals Mind Po-lice. Lightnin' scams the Mind Po-lice, scoots on outa there.

Has another pull on the bottle.

Gets back down to pickin'.

Not cotton. Gueetar.

Shit, he ain't never stopped, pickin'.

See: there's the bluesman done his mama bad, and the
bluesman his mama done him bad. Lightnin', wiry, bent over
his guitar, dark mirror shades, gold-toothed smile flashing, is
the first, he cain't hep it, but he knows what it means to be the
second, twisted around his guitar, fingering the chain-gang
scars on his legs, contorted death-mask face, discordant
tender strumming, knows what it means to be without.

Like "Ball of Twine," about a black woman whose mind is
twisted like a ball of twine and Lightnin' sure "wisht I could

do somethin' to change that woman mind," he sings, "to hep her."*

Lord have mercy.

1986. Artist has a form/content. S/he encodes the form/ content with a key. S/he transmits the form/content to the consumer. Consumer decodes the form/content with the same (or with another) key. Form/content is now commodity. Every- one grins. White small teeth. *Cut my brother down.*

Lightnin' says this song is "dedicated to the whole world. To the womens especially."* As for the mens, they should just listen to what he sings. Riffs dreamy riffs bass baritone dark shades gold smile dangling cigarette. Lightnin's gwine build hissef a heaven for all the lovin' womens of the world. So as to give them a happy home. "And a man ain't allowed in there." Heaven reminds Lightnin' of Jesus, who, Lightnin' sings, ain't no better then him. Hell, Lightnin' knows jus' as much as He do. The "best thing we bofe could do," Lightnin' sings, "is pray."*

"I woke up this moanin'."
Hell, Bourgeois dint never get to sleep.
Watchin' TV.
Looking at the screen (through his mind) at the lynchmen's faces, lynchwomen too, lynchchildren, Easter-seal complex- ions, flat-faced / high-boned, telegenic lynchfolk, mugging for the camera, live oak, dark-skinned boy twisting, canned laugh- ter, dogwood, the too-sweet night, as if every God-fearing- pink-skinned-consumer-racist sprayed her (it's always *her* in this scenario) Johnson and Johnson air freshener on com- mand.

Little Brother Montgomery sings: "The first time I met the blues, mama, they came walking through the woods, / The first time I met the blues, baby, they came walking through the woods, / They stopped at my house first, mama, and done me all the harm they could."**

Thas right, black bluesman go after yo' ass with a razor, you cross 'im.

WHY CAN'T THEY MURDER LIKE CIVILIZED PEO-PLE?

Lightnin' don't know about no God, but he sure as shit know about the posse.

Posse, I'm talkin' at you, switch off your TV.

Now stare at the eyes of your head in the dead screen-turned-mirror.

Feel with your thick-fingered work-hand the lean of your wallet in your hip pocket.

Think, think.

Stash your guns, ropes, ax-handles, bomb-fixin's in your pickup.

Your broad-shouldered G.M.C. pickup (you be payin' it off for a great long time).

Got some grime on it from backcountry-wetback-bounty-chasing.

Posse, set down right yere near the fire.

Bourgeois gonna sing yawl a story.

(Where's my dog-eared Whitman?

Where's my shit-transfiguring blue guitar?)

Don't look at me look at your own bad self in the fire just listen.

"Nobody can sing the blues if he never *been* blued."†

Thas right, singin' of clear sight and resistance.

Swallow their glittery shell but spit it up lasers.

Set your booby traps for the boobies.

Keeping one sharp eye on their pharmaceuticals.

Call to arms / via AT&T any color you want any fragrance I want mine to smell like Madonna's 700-foot—

"Bourgeois, where and when do I plant the freakin' charge?"

Do this cousin strap it to your body while you boogy eat imported cheese phone your broker sidestep the AIDS victim."

"Down in Lou'siana,
I ast the bossman let my baby be."*
I got in my brand new G.M.C. pickup.
Rode right upside the bossman's wallet.
Now I'm a fugitive from justice.
Yeah now I'm a fugitive from that rope they call justice.
Lord have mercy.
When they get me gonna lynch me.
What happens I load my brand new G.M.C. pickup with charge?
Blow the bossmens up real high.
Up into the pink fat lap of heaven (since they already done bought it and painted it *their* color).
What happens we all buy brand new G.M.C. pickups on credit like we suppose to, load our trucks up with charge, blow all the bossmens up to their heaven, only make sure we jump out first, we ain't doin' it for the Pink-Outhouse-On-The-Plantation later but for our sisters and brothers right now, I'm just wonderin' what happens, love sure don't work.
"You're confusin' yo'sef, Bourgeois. This 'charge' we talkin' 'bout *is* love, it's the on'y shit thas left."

Inside, the black-felon is about to be executed with a lethal injection. Outside, the capital punishment advocates are male caucasian criminal science students from nearby Sam Houston State College. They wave posters which say "KILL 'EM IN VEIN" or "JUSTICE FINALLY PREVAILS." One student's poster says simply "DEATH," except that in the lower right-hand corner is a "Hi, Mom."

"You know, I woke up this moanin, woke up in the county jail.
I ast the jailer bring me the key.
The jailer said, 'Lightnin', I ain't gonna bring you no key.' "*
The jailer said he reckoned they was gonna lynch me.
I ast him bring me my gueetar.
Which, pickin', is the blues I been singin' to yawl out there.
Cut him cut my brother down.

And I don't mean plant him in the ground.
He's alive and close-to-death-clear-sighted-mad-as-hell.
I said my brother and sister near death so long are ready.
Are you?
Lord have mercy.
Are you all?

---

*Lightnin' Hopkins' words, either in recorded conversation or in song. Sam (Lightnin') Hopkins, 1912–1982, blues guitarist and vocalist out of Centerville, Texas.

**Little Brother Montgomery's verse is cited in Houston A. Baker, Jr., *Blues, Ideology, and Afro-American Literature: A Vernacular Theory* (The University of Chicago Press, 1984).

†Spoken by J. B. Lenoir, blues guitarist-vocalist, 1929–67.

POSTSCRIPT

MAX HEADROOM

"One day in Silicon Valley I came upon two
blind men, well-dressed, sitting side by side,
each masturbating the other."

ZERO OPTION

A 44-year-old woman, described by her daughter as "emotionally distraught," walked into an elementary school classroom on Tuesday morning and fatally shot herself in front of 23 fifth-graders.

The 23 pupils in Dry Ice Fog Elementary School of Sector 3 and Ms. Bernice (called "Bunny") Bornagin, their red-haired teacher, tried to dissuade the woman, who was armed with two Smith & Wesson .32 caliber revolvers. "I'm sorry I have to do it this way," the woman said before firing a bullet into her head.

When it was clear that the woman would not listen to reason, Ms. Bornagin instructed her students to stare at the side-by-side TV monitors above the blackboard at the front of the room, school officials said. The first time the woman, identified as Missy Rodriguez, pulled the trigger of the gun in her right hand, it misfired, so she aimed the gun in her left hand at the wall, fired a shot, then pointed the gun in her left hand at her left temple and fired the fatal shot.

Psychologists from the Jesu-Manville Sector were transmitted to Dry Ice Fog Elementary at once to begin counseling the pupils. The psychologists were dressed in camouflage fatigues. The pupils received them at their consoles while eating their lunch, with the principal's permission, since it was a special occasion: TV News was running a 30-second segment on the classroom suicide.

"Very few [pupils] actually saw anything," said Harvey Joy, a high school principal in the Sector, a former principal of Dry Ice Fog Elementary, and a psychologist in his own right. "Most of the pupils talked about it as though it was something they'd seen on TV," Dr. Joy said. "Each pupil will handle it differently. I was very impressed with the calmness of the pupils."

The woman was declared dead at Sector 3 Hospital at 11:17 a.m., about an hour after the shooting. School officials said there was absolutely no evidence that Rodriguez, the suicide, had any connection with Dry Ice Fog Elementary. Rodriguez was not a parent of any of the school's 412 students. "She was a shy sort of person," Rodriguez' 27-year-old daughter Hortensia said.

The parents of the 23 fifth-graders in Sector 3 have met with their attorneys to discuss filing a dual lawsuit (the figure reportedly was 19 million dollars) against Dry Ice Fog Elementary for inadequate surveillance, and against Hortensia Rodriguez Cora, the sole living relative of the suicide.

"Very few of the pupils, if any, saw anything," Dr. Joy emphasized. "Ms. Bornagin instructed them to stare at the TV monitors above the blackboards, and our indications are that the pupils followed instructions and watched a videotape of themselves at their consoles accessing the geography of Mexico. Nonetheless, the suicide was demonstrably traumatic, and the parents of the 23 fifth-graders in Sector 3 are constitutionally entitled to sue."

20 MINUTES INTO THE FUTURE

"There's a real feeling that some of our foreign competitors have eaten our lunch," said Rep. Don Ritter (R-Pa.), who chairs a Task Force on High Technology & Competitiveness. "We can't let that happen in superconductors."

Die- Die- Die- Die- DIET PEPSI!

"The shopping mall is the natural venue for lip sync and air band competitions. Though malls tend to look alike, different malls in different neighborhoods attract contestants with different tastes. 'Like in Brooklyn you get a lot of break dancing and rapping,' said Dickie. 'But you go to Levittown and you get punk—there's a big punk club there called Spit. And in Staten Island there's more, like, commercial New Wave.'"

The crowning irony, according to Newsweek, *is that, "for all his scoffing at the system, Max is, in actuality, the quintessential product of his times—a pop icon designed and manufactured for the video generation with an almost mathematical precision."*

Where you from?
Pakistan.
You mean Pakestine?
No.
I think you do, listen up: Pakestine craves Diet Pepsi, that freakin' heat plus your bean-eaters' propensity to put on a pound or two.

Brad likes Lite Beer, scented candles and environmental music, and plenty of it. Anton lurches towards the synthesizer:

Bach's Toccata in B. *Above: monitoring satellites and waste disposal modules. And that's how the lifestyle of the Beverly Hills male influences your Japanese designer.*

Bind their long hair one to the other, strip them, blind them, grant them long knives, call the survivor TERRORIST. Not long knives but canes, sword-canes, actually sugar cane, they're "undocumented," with bound-to-the-other black coarse hair, each made-blind farmhand a TERRORIST, the survivor alone called Cain.

"Increasingly the trend is towards large automated systems— so-called Flexible Manufacturing Systems—controlled by software written in specialized programming language. This naturally enables robots to perform complex and coordinated actions, and to mimic more closely the flexibility and respon- siveness of the non-robotic worker."

How much do you and your lover trust each other, really? These soft ribbons add extra spice to "trust me" fantasy games with that special someone. Unlike other restraints that may chafe and irritate, we selected our tethers of trust es- pecially for their comfort, softness and sensuality. Each set contains two wrist and two ankle tethers, the clasps are velcro, the ribbons are nylon parachute webbing 48-inches long for ultimate versatility, scented.

Diet Pepsi technicians have now successfully demythicized the romantic mumbo-jumbo of the human brain, which fundamen- tally is no more than a binary system of off-on switches, and employing immaculate logic, the Pepsi team has isolated the consumer principle in a "computer-generated" image, which replicates tone without temperament, which is at once the consummate image and the consummate reproduction of im-

ages, and which, despite its "marginal humanness," is sexy.

WARGASM

A 44-year-old *Hispanic* woman, described by her daughter as "emotionally distraught," walked into an elementary school classroom on Tuesday morning and fatally shot herself in front of 23 fifth-graders.

The 23 pupils in Dry Ice Fog Elementary School of Sector 3, and Ms. Bernice (called "Bunny") Bornagin, their red-haired *diet-Pepsi-thin* teacher, tried to dissuade the woman, who was armed with two *evidently stolen* Smith & Wesson .32 caliber revolvers. "I'm sorry I have to do it this way," the woman said *in heavily-accented English* before firing a bullet into her head.

When it was clear that the woman would not listen to reason, Ms. Bornagin instructed her students to stare at the side-by-side TV monitors above the blackboard at the front of the room, school officials said. The first time the woman, identified as Missy Rodriguez, *and overweight,* pulled the trigger of the gun in her right hand, it misfired, so she aimed the gun in her left hand at the wall, fired a shot, then pointed the gun in her left hand at her left temple and fired the fatal shot.

Psychologists from the Jesu-Manville Sector were transmitted to Dry Ice Fog Elementary at once to begin counseling the pupils. The psychologists were dressed in camouflage fatigues, *called "terrorist couture."* The pupils received them at their consoles while eating their lunch, with the principal's permission, since this was a special occasion: TV News was running a 30-second segment on the *overweight Hispanic's* classroom suicide, *and the box lunches were donated by Sharper Image, Inc., a sponsor of the news segment, along with Pepsi. Her mom was always "moping," the suicide's daughter said.*

"Very few [pupils] actually saw anything," said Harvey Joy, a high school principal in the Sector, a former principal of Dry Ice Fog Elementary, and a psychologist in his own right. "Most of the pupils talked about it as though it was something they'd seen on TV," Dr. Joy said. "Each pupil will handle it differently. I was very impressed with the calmness of the pupils."

The woman was declared dead at Sector 3 Hospital *"For Indigents"* at 11:17 a.m., about an hour after the shooting. School officials said there was absolutely no evidence that Rodriguez, the suicide, had any connection with Dry Ice Fog Elementary. *The preliminary indications are that she was an "Illegal" from El Salvador and that the two guns were stolen in El Salvador or elsewhere in that area.* Rodriguez was not a parent of any of the school's 412 students. *"We only have three Hispanic pupils in the school,"* an official said. *"And obviously we keep a complete file on the parents of these pupils."* "She was a sort of shy person," Rodriguez' 27-year-old daughter Hortensia said. *"She was trying to find work and couldn't. My mom had a problem sticking with a job once she got it,"* Hortensia said.

The parents of the 23 fifth-graders in Sector 3 have met with their attorneys to discuss filing a dual law suit (the figure reportedly was 19 million dollars) against Dry Ice Fog Elementary for inadequate surveillance, and against Hortensia Rodriguez Cora, the sole living relative of the suicide *in the U.S. Cora's husband is unemployed and they have three young children. Dry Ice Fog is a Type C "private" institution, established in the throes of the Civil Rights struggles when concerned parents of middle-class white children struck out for an alternative to violent public schooling in the inner cities.*

"Very few of the pupils, if any, saw anything," Dr. Joy emphasized. "Ms. Bornagin instructed them to stare at the TV monitors above the blackboards, and our indications are that the pupils followed instructions and watched a videotape of themselves at their consoles accessing the geography of Mexico. Nonetheless, the *overweight Illegal Alien's* suicide was demonstrably traumatic, and the parents of the 23 fifth graders in Sector 3 are constitutionally entitled to sue *not only the Illegal Alien's heirs but also, according to experts in International Law, the Marxist-Leninist government of El Salvador.*"